STAR WARS™

JEDI VS. SITH

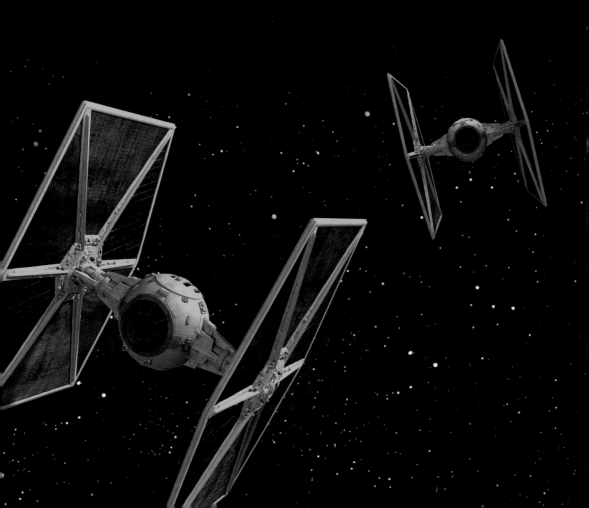

CONTENTS

STAR WARS™

JEDI VS. SITH

JEDI
TIMELINE

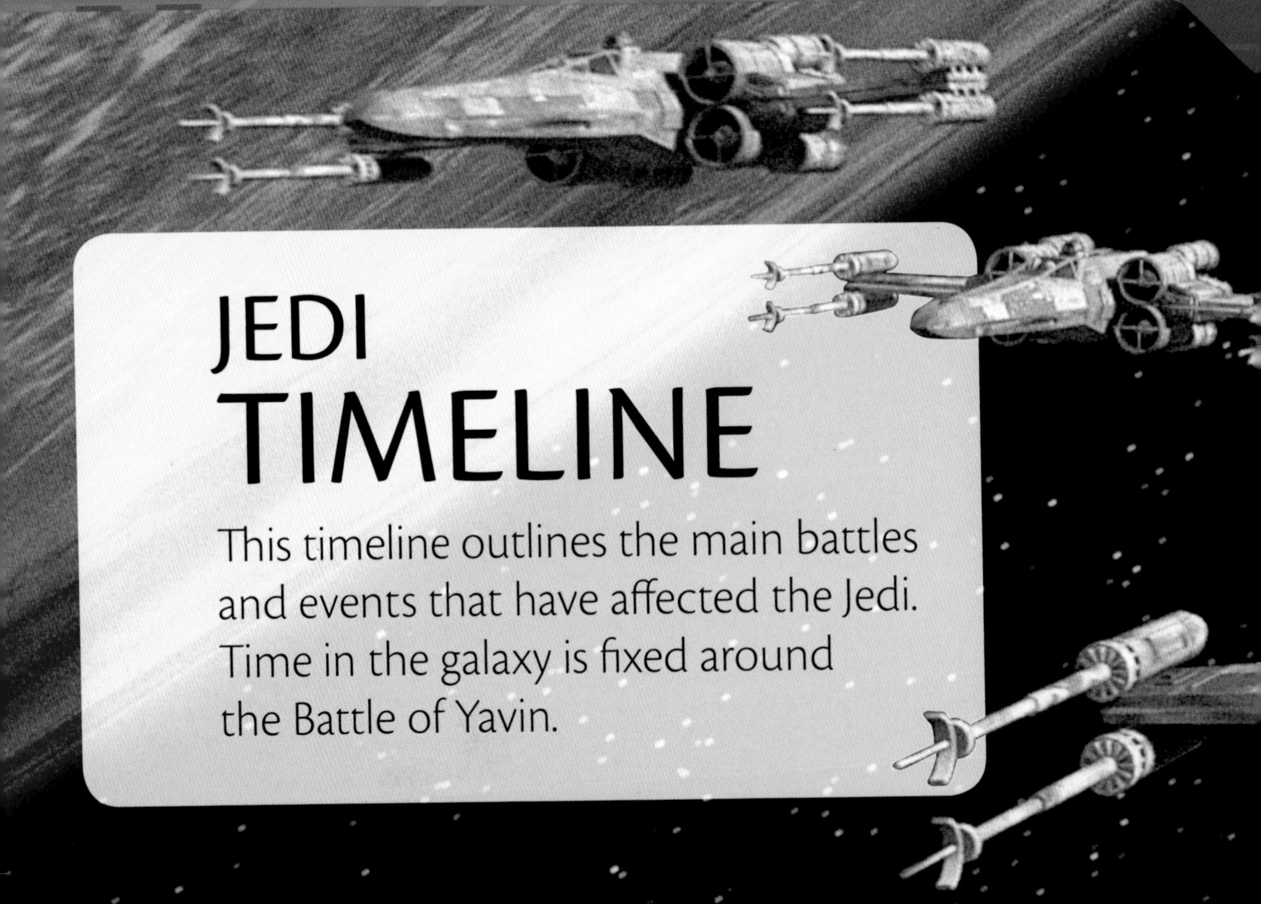

This timeline outlines the main battles and events that have affected the Jedi. Time in the galaxy is fixed around the Battle of Yavin.

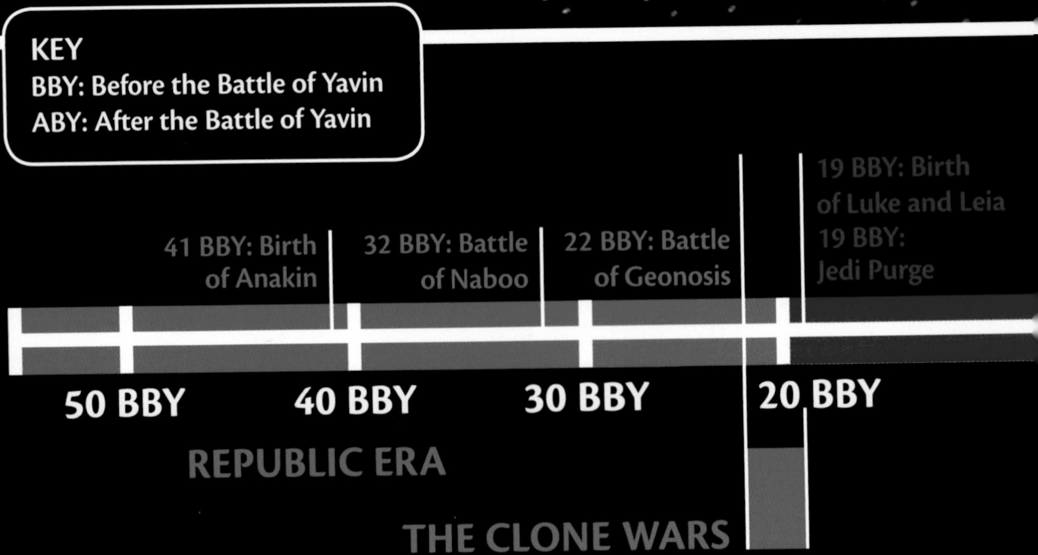

KEY
BBY: Before the Battle of Yavin
ABY: After the Battle of Yavin

19 BBY: Birth
of Luke and Leia
19 BBY:
Jedi Purge

41 BBY: Birth
of Anakin

32 BBY: Battle
of Naboo

22 BBY: Battle
of Geonosis

50 BBY   **40 BBY**   **30 BBY**   **20 BBY**

REPUBLIC ERA

THE CLONE WARS

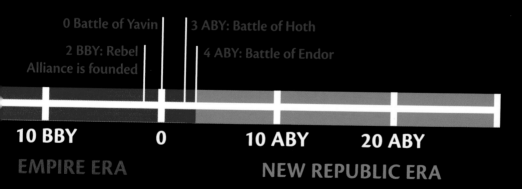

0 Battle of Yavin   3 ABY: Battle of Hoth

2 BBY: Rebel   4 ABY: Battle of Endor
Alliance is founded

10 BBY   **0**   **10 ABY**   **20 ABY**

EMPIRE ERA   **NEW REPUBLIC ERA**

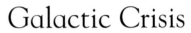

Galactic Crisis

In a galaxy far, far away, a great and peaceful Republic existed. It was governed by the Senate—a group of representatives from each planet in the Republic. The representatives, called senators, met in a Senate building on the capital planet of Coruscant. Strong Jedi Knights kept the peace in the Republic.

The Jedi tried to ensure that planets sorted out any arguments by peaceful negotiation. They used a mysterious energy called the Force, and carried glowing lightsabers to defend themselves when negotiation failed.

Sadly, peace in the Republic would be destroyed. A greedy business organization called the Trade Federation had created an army of machine-soldiers called battle droids. They began to invade planets, starting with a small world called Naboo. As the conflict grew, the Republic had to deploy a massive army to defend itself. War soon erupted in the galaxy.

But all was not what it seemed. Both sides would discover that they had been manipulated by an evil Sith Lord named Darth Sidious who wanted to destroy the Jedi and rule the galaxy!

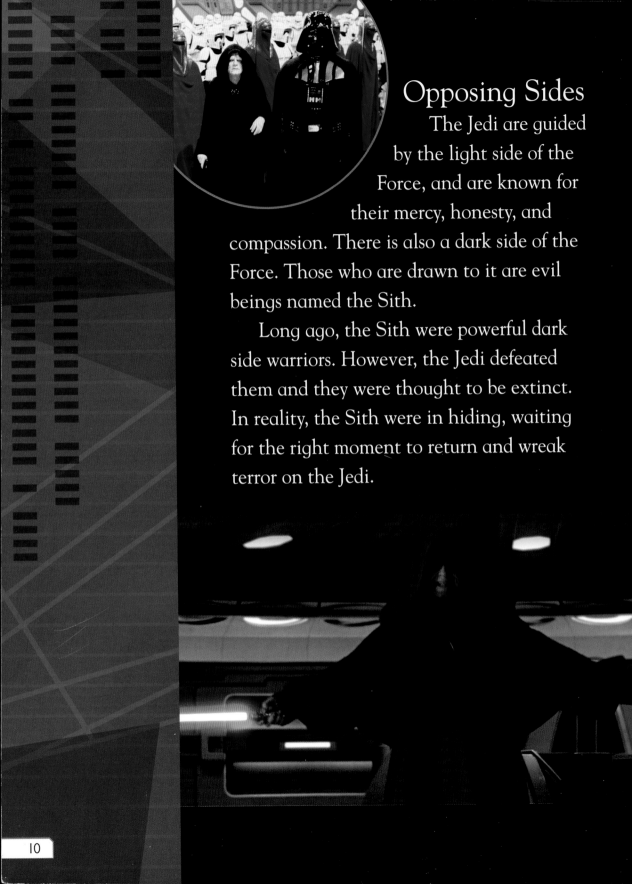

Opposing Sides

The Jedi are guided by the light side of the Force, and are known for their mercy, honesty, and compassion. There is also a dark side of the Force. Those who are drawn to it are evil beings named the Sith.

Long ago, the Sith were powerful dark side warriors. However, the Jedi defeated them and they were thought to be extinct. In reality, the Sith were in hiding, waiting for the right moment to return and wreak terror on the Jedi.

Sith Lord Darth Sidious was secretly in control of the Trade Federation, which was run by greedy Neimoidian aliens. He wanted the organization to start a war that would put him in power as Emperor and force every planet to obey him. For years Sidious had kept his Sith identity and his master plan secret, fooling everyone by pretending to be a kindly politician named Senator Palpatine.

Palpatine used his position in the Senate to manipulate the other planet leaders, tricking his way into becoming Supreme Chancellor. Only a brave and determined few—with the Jedi among them—would refuse to accept Palpatine's evil rule. They had to be prepared to fight many epic battles if they were to bring peace and justice to the galaxy.

Jedi Training

The Jedi Order is an ancient peacekeeping organization. All Jedi have to learn to live by the Jedi Code—a set of rules that they must obey. According to the Code, the Jedi must use the Force for good. They should have compassion for every form of life, and should engage in combat only to defend others or themselves.

It takes years to become a Jedi Knight and so training usually begins at a very early age. In order to follow the Code it is

important that
young Jedi, known
as Younglings,
learn to remain
calm and focused in
stressful situations.
Younglings are
taught to use
lightsabers as well
as techniques for
fighting skillfully
in a duel. At times

their eyes are covered while they train;
that way they can learn to feel the Force
and use their instincts, instead of relying
on what they can see.

Older trainees, called Padawans, also
learn how to use the Force to move objects
without touching them. A Force pull
enables Jedi to bring something to
them. A Force push is a powerful
technique that repels objects or
opponents. To help them in battle,
Jedi must also learn to be
physically strong, fit, and agile.

THE LIFE OF A JEDI

It takes years of hard work to become a full-fledged Jedi. Trainees undergo difficult tests under the watchful eye of a skilled Master of the Force.

JEDI HIGH COUNCIL

The Council is made up of 12 of the greatest Jedi Masters. They resolve disputes, make decisions, and uphold the Jedi Code.

YOUNGLING

Those who show Force potential are selected by the Council to begin Jedi training. The Younglings are taken to the Jedi Temple, where they live while studying the basics of the Force.

Grand Master Yoda

GRAND MASTER

A Jedi Master must be exceptional to reach this rank. As Grand Master, Yoda was head of the whole Jedi Order.

*Padawan
Anakin Skywalker*

PADAWAN
If a Youngling works hard, they will be selected by a Jedi to be their Padawan. The Jedi becomes the Padawan's Master and the pair will travel together and carry out one-to-one training.

*Jedi Knight
Aayla
Secura*

*Jedi Master
Luminara
Unduli*

JEDI KNIGHT
Those who pass the Trials become qualified Jedi Knights. They can go on their own missions and even train their own Padawan.

JEDI MASTER
Once a Jedi Knight has trained a Padawan, they can be promoted to Jedi Master. If they show great skill and devotion, they may be invited to sit on the Jedi High Council.

The Lightsaber

Since ancient times, the lightsaber has been the chosen weapon of the Jedi Knights. The user must be experienced in the ways of the Force in order to wield it skillfully in combat.

A lightsaber is held like a sword but, instead of a metal blade, a lightsaber has a beam of energy that bursts from the handle when the weapon is ignited. Lightsabers can

easily cut through the toughest of material—even metal doors—but not the blade of another lightsaber. The powerful lightsaber has other important uses in combat.
Jedi can use the Force to predict incoming energy bolts from blaster guns and then use a lightsaber to deflect the bolts back toward their opponent.

The Sith also use lightsabers in combat. Sometimes their weapons are even double-bladed, which suits their aggressive style of fighting.

TOOLS OF
THE TRADE

A Jedi does not require many tools. Everything they need is carried in a utility belt, which also holds their lightsaber. They wear simple clothes and tough boots for missions and battles.

COMLINK
A security-enhanced comlink is used to talk to other Jedi. Its encoders ensure messages cannot be intercepted.

LIGHTSABER
All Jedi lightsabers follow a similar design. Each Jedi builds their own lightsaber to complement their fighting technique.

HOLOPROJECTOR
This device can send and receive secure 3-D holotransmissions via a comlink to be viewed in real time.

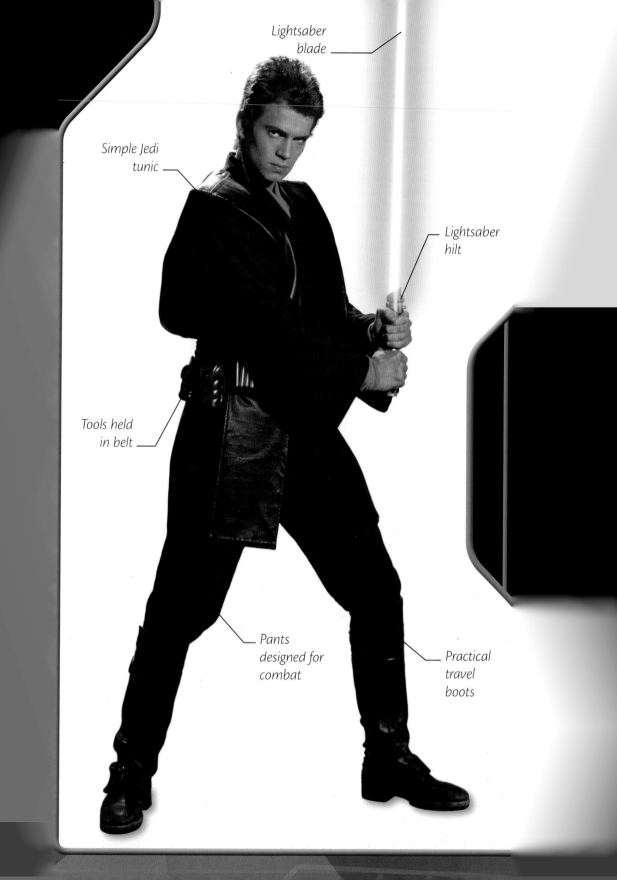

Lightsaber
blade

Simple Jedi
tunic

Lightsaber
hilt

Tools held
in belt

Pants
designed for
combat

Practical
travel
boots

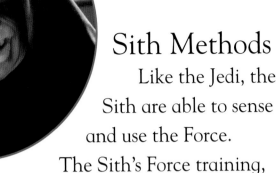

Sith Methods

Like the Jedi, the
Sith are able to sense
and use the Force.
The Sith's Force training,
however, varies greatly from that of the Jedi.
They use the dark side of the Force and gain
their power from raw emotions such as anger
and hatred. The Sith do not value life or
feel compassion, and their ferocious style
of combat reflects their violent attitudes.

The Sith act
in aggression
and not in
defense, and
are prepared
to do anything
in battle—
no matter
how devious.
The Sith
always come in pairs—a Master and an
apprentice. Knowledge of the dark side
of the Force is passed on from Master
to apprentice.

The Sith can use the Force to produce lethal Force lightning. They channel the Force through their bodies and discharge powerful bolts of energy from their palms and fingertips into their opponents.

The Sith can also channel the power of the Force to choke a victim without actually touching them. This deadly combat technique is known as the Force choke.

TWO-FACED

Senator Palpatine was really the most powerful Sith Lord in the galaxy. As a senator, he appeared to be kind and supportive—but as the leader of the Sith, he was evil and hungry for power.

"There is no civility, only politics."

Senator Palpatine

SENATOR PALPATINE
Senator Palpatine received praise from the Jedi Order for his wisdom. The Jedi were unaware that he was controlling the Senate for his own good.

"Only through me can you achieve a power greater than any Jedi. Learn to know the dark side of the Force."

Darth Sidious

DARTH SIDIOUS

As Sith Lord Darth Sidious, Palpatine ruled over his subjects with fear. But he always concealed his face, so that no one could discover his secret.

LAND BATTLES
Soldiers must be prepared for combat on a rough and varied terrain. Troops utilize specialized vehicles and artillery, and must stay alert in case of sudden attacks.

Grass Plains Battle

Even the most peaceful species will fight to defend their planet. The Gungans were a water-dwelling species who lived on Naboo, a planet of swamps and grasslands. They were known for avoiding contact with the Naboo people and for their dislike of conflict. That was before the Trade Federation invaded Naboo with an army of battle droids, under the secret orders of Darth Sidious. With their planet at stake, the Gungans were forced to take up arms and work with the Naboo people and the Jedi.

The Gungans had not raised an army for over a hundred years, but they did not falter. Their job was to

lure the droid forces away from the Naboo
capital, Theed, so that the Jedi could move
in and fight the Trade Federation there.

The scene of the battle was an area
named the Great Grass Plains. Assembled
on the plains, the Gungan Grand Army
faced a massive army of battle droids, which
were being controlled by a Trade Federation
spaceship. It was a scary sight! Would the
Gungans' battle skills be enough to compete?

Gungan battle tactics relied heavily on defense. They chose battle sites near swamps, so that if they retreated their foes could not follow. On the battlefield their first move was to deploy huge energy shields. The shields were activated by machines carried on the backs of giant swamp lizards named fambaas. These energy shields were great for protecting

armies from enemy missiles, but on the Great Grass Plains the Gungans discovered that they had a serious weakness. Battle

droids could walk right through them!

Under fire from droid blasters, the
Gungans responded with their traditional
weapons—plasma balls filled with explosive
energy, which they hurled into the air with
catapults and throwing sticks. Glowing,
handheld energy shields protected them
against blaster bolts.

The Gungans could not defeat all the
battle droids, but they hoped to engage them
long enough for their Jedi allies to strike
elsewhere. Their strategy was successful! Out
in space, a Naboo pilot blew up the Droid
Control Ship, and the battle droids were
stopped in their tracks.

WHO ARE THE
GUNGANS?

This swamp-dwelling race lives in the underwater city of Otoh Gunga, located deep within Lake Paonga on Naboo. Though a peaceful race, Gungans are capable of combat, and use plasma-based weapons in battle.

OTOH GUNGA
Otoh Gunga is made up of a cluster of giant bubbles held together by special machines.

Jar Jar Binks

This clumsy Gungan once lived in a swamp near Otoh Gunga. Jar Jar became good friends with Jedi Master Qui-Gon Jinn.

WHO RULES THE GUNGANS?
Boss Nass is the ruler of Otoh Gunga. When Separatists attacked Naboo, he assembled a massive army from Gungan settlements to fight the enemy.

Battle of Geonosis

To battle its enemies' huge droid armies, the Republic recruited a ready-made army of its own. It was made up of millions of clone troopers, all identical copies of a single ultimate soldier.

The clone army first saw action on the planet of Geonosis, in a battle that would

force Jedi Master Yoda to become a military general against his peaceful instincts.

Jedi Obi-Wan Kenobi and Anakin Skywalker had been captured by the Separatists and faced execution in an arena on Geonosis along with Senator Padmé Amidala of Naboo. When a Jedi rescue attempt was initiated, the Separatists unleashed hordes of super battle droids in the arena. Could the clone army stop these droids and save the Jedi? Led by Master Yoda, the clones came to the rescue. A massive battle ensued—one that soon spread outside the arena. Many Jedi and clones were destroyed, but eventually the droids retreated. The Battle of Geonosis was the first conflict in what later became known as the Clone Wars.

SEPARATIST DROIDS

Big corporations like the Trade Federation supplied the money to build the droid army for the Separatists. The Separatists used these unrelenting soldiers to fight their battles.

DROIDEKA
Droidekas are fast, deadly, destroyer droids. They attack by curling into a wheel shape and rolling at their enemies with terrifying speed.

Twin blaster cannons

HAILFIRE DROID

Hailfire droids are armed with two racks of deadly missiles. Enemies who avoid these may be crushed under their enormous wheels.

Laser cannon

Two missile launchers

Fragile construction

Thick armor

Built-in laser cannon

SUPER BATTLE DROID

These droids are bigger, tougher versions of regular battle droids. They carry more powerful weapons, and are harder to destroy.

BATTLE DROID

These droid soldiers are programmed to blindly obey orders. Cheap and expendable, they are produced by the million.

SPIDER DROID

Spider droids come in many forms. They range from burrowing dwarf types to homing spider droids who stalk the battlefields on long, extendable legs.

Heavy blaster cannon

Can cross rough ground

Battle of Kashyyyk

One of the biggest battles of the Clone Wars—and also one of the biggest turning points—took place on Kashyyyk. This thickly forested planet was home to tall, furry creatures called Wookiees, who were firm allies of the Republic. The Wookiees fought bravely alongside the clone troopers, battling the Separatist tanks and droids on land and on water. Victory on Kashyyyk seemed certain, but then disaster struck.

Chancellor Palpatine had secretly brainwashed the clone troopers to switch sides when they received a signal named

Order 66. When this signal was given, clones everywhere turned their weapons on their Jedi generals. Nearly all the Jedi leaders were killed, although Yoda escaped with the help of brave Wookiee chieftain Tarfful.

The clones obeyed only Sith orders now, and when Darth Sidious became Emperor he made them his personal army—the dreaded stormtroopers. The Empire was born!

Battle of Hoth

The Empire ruled the
galaxy with an iron grip,
but many brave people
struggled to overthrow it.
They were known as the Rebel Alliance,
and Emperor Palpatine and Sith Lord Darth
Vader directed much of the Empire's military
strength toward crushing them.

The rebels operated out of a secret base
in a converted ice cave on the frozen planet
of Hoth. When Darth Vader discovered the
base, he attacked it with great force.
The battle that followed left the
rebel cause reeling.

Central to the Empire's attack were AT-ATs—giant walking tanks armed with blasters. The rebels could not stop these monstrous tanks with their guns and lasers. Although the rebels brought down two of them in a daring maneuver using trip cables, they were finally forced to flee, leaving their base to Darth Vader and his stormtroopers.

The Battle of Hoth was a disaster for the rebels, but it was not the end. Pilot Han Solo escaped in his spaceship, the *Millennium Falcon*, with Princess Leia, C-3PO, and Chewbacca.

CLONE TROOPER TO
STORMTROOPER

Clone troopers of the Galactic Republic were constantly upgraded with better armor and equipment. When Palpatine built the Empire, the clones got their biggest change of all. Transformed into Imperial stormtroopers, they were given brand-new armor, and a brand-new role— destroying the Emperor's enemies.

Helmet design based on Jango Fett's helmet

DC-15A blaster rifle

Armor made up of 20 separate pieces

PHASE 1: CLONE TROOPER
Troopers of the Republic Army initially wore identical white armor that was bulky and uncomfortable.

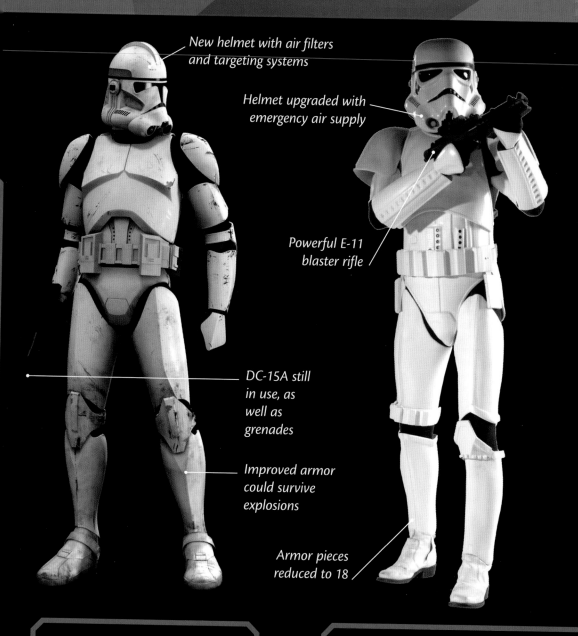

New helmet with air filters and targeting systems

Helmet upgraded with emergency air supply

Powerful E-11 blaster rifle

DC-15A still in use, as well as grenades

Improved armor could survive explosions

Armor pieces reduced to 18

PHASE 2: STORMTROOPER
Stronger, more flexible armor was worn by the clone troopers who became the first stormtroopers.

IMPERIAL STORMTROOPER
The final version of the Imperial stormtrooper armor had fewer individual pieces, to aid efficiency.

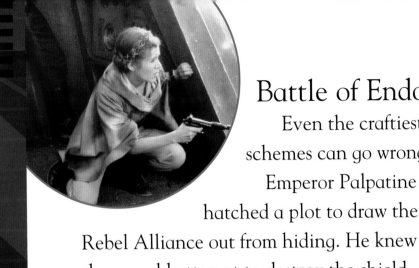

Battle of Endor

Even the craftiest schemes can go wrong! Emperor Palpatine hatched a plot to draw the Rebel Alliance out from hiding. He knew they would attempt to destroy the shield generator on the forest moon of Endor, which protected his massive battle station, named the Death Star. When a rebel team led by Luke Skywalker, Princess Leia, Han Solo, and the Wookiee ally named Chewbacca landed on Endor the Imperial army was ready for them. But it was not ready for their allies—furry creatures called Ewoks.

The little Ewoks took the stormtroopers by surprise. They did not have sophisticated weapons, but they knew how to fight in a forest, hurling rocks at the stormtroopers, leaving them in disarray. The rebels were able to destroy the shield generator, allowing their space fleet to attack the Death Star in a battle that would signal the end of the Empire.

SPACE BATTLES

Pilots face great danger in space battles, as they can be attacked from all sides. They need to show bravery as well as skill and, in most cases, experience helps.

Naboo Space Battle

When the native people of Naboo entered battle with the evil Trade Federation, starfighters were their best spacecraft for the space-based part of the conflict. The ships are aerodynamic, agile, and fast. In defense, the Trade Federation's ring-shaped Droid Control Ship unleashed deadly vulture droid ships on the starfighters.

An experienced pilot is usually essential, but one of the starfighter pilots was a nine-year-old boy named Anakin Skywalker. He was hiding in a starfighter that was docked on Naboo when the spacecraft accidentally took off into space.

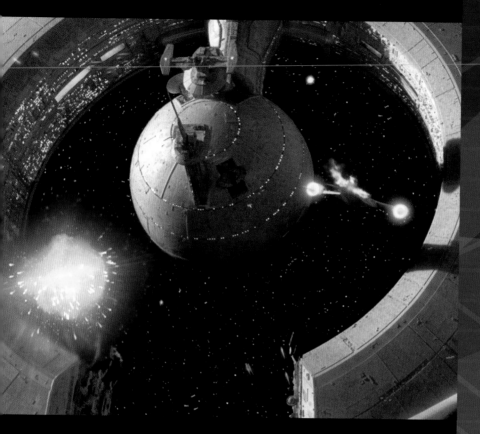

Bravery is required by the Jedi in any
type of conflict and when caught up in
a dangerous space battle, young Anakin
showed a natural boldness. He was able to
enter the Droid Control Ship, avoiding deadly
laser blasts, and fire torpedoes into its reactor.
Anakin escaped when the massive ship
exploded. The ship had sent signals to every
battle droid on Naboo. Droids only follow
orders, so as the Control Ship was destroyed,
they automatically stopped functioning.

SPACECRAFT FACT FILE

In space fights, spacecraft of various shapes and sizes engage in battle. The Separatists and the Empire employ anything from tiny droids to massive Star Destroyers to fight off their enemies in space, but the Jedi prefer flying smaller starfighters.

.... Solar arrays

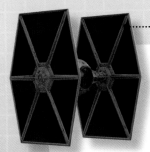

TIE FIGHTER
Length: 9 m (29 ft)
Weapons: Laser cannons
Built by: Sienar Fleet Systems

Hull protected by shield generators

SLAVE I
Length: 21.15 m (95.75 ft)
Weapons: Laser cannons, ion cannons
Built by: Kuat Systems Engineering

Heavily armored

Shiny chromium finish ....

NABOO J-TYPE BARGE
Length: 39 m (128 ft)
Weapons: None
Built by: Theed Palace Space Vessel Engineering Corps

IMPERIAL STAR DESTROYER

Length: 1,600 m (5,249 ft)
Weapons: Turbolaser batteries, heavy ion cannons
Built by: Kuat Drive Yards

Droids starfighters do not require pilots ......

VULTURE DROID

Length: 6.96 m (22.75 ft)
Weapons: Laser cannon, energy torpedoes
Built by: Xi Char Cathedral Factories

Can carry several starfighters

Space for one pilot ....

ETA-2 ACTIS STARFIGHTER

Length: 5.47 m (17.94 ft)
Weapons: Laser cannons, seismic mines, torpedoes
Built by: Kuat Systems Engineering

DELTA-7B STARFIGHTER

Length: 8 m (26.2 ft)
Weapons: Laser cannons
Built by: Kuat Systems Engineering

Can hold a Jedi and an astromech droid

The Clone Wars

Some space battles involve two ships in a duel, which is known as a dogfight. In others, many different ships do battle with each other.

When full-scale war broke out between the Republic and the Separatist droid army, there was a spectacular space conflict above the planet Coruscant, home of the Jedi Temple. Separatist droid fighters engaged Republic starfighters, while each side's huge warships blasted away at each other. Both sides lost many vessels in the dramatic and explosive battle.

Obi-Wan Kenobi and Anakin Skywalker had gained a reputation as the best pilots in the galaxy, but they still struggled with the sheer number of ships trying to destroy them.

They piloted their fast Interceptor starfighters, dodging enemy fire together with extreme skill. But they faced many challenges. Small buzz droids attached themselves to the side of Obi-Wan's ship to inflict damage with their cutting arms.

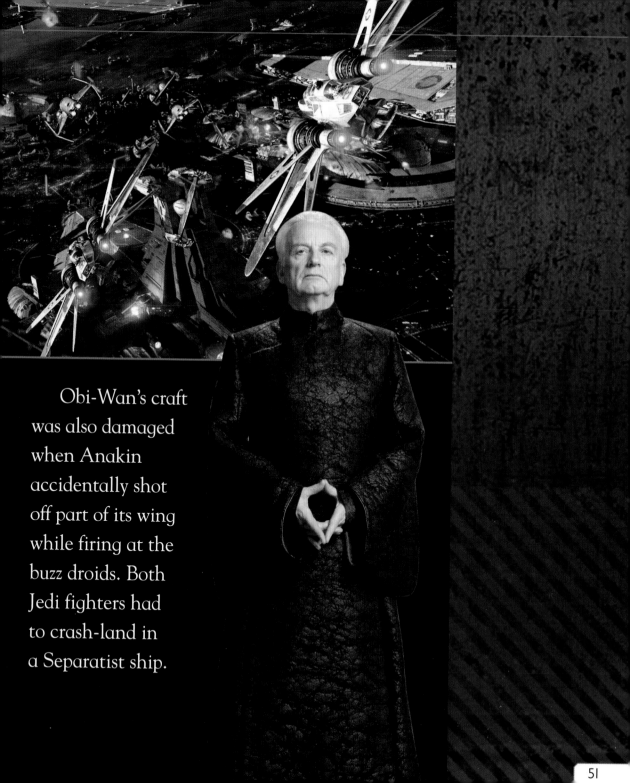

Obi-Wan's craft was also damaged when Anakin accidentally shot off part of its wing while firing at the buzz droids. Both Jedi fighters had to crash-land in a Separatist ship.

Rebel Ship

Rebel Han Solo's ship, the *Millennium Falcon*, was deployed in many dogfights across the galaxy. Though the *Falcon* was heavily battle-scarred from its many space adventures, it could still outmaneuver most enemy craft. In a tricky situation, the *Falcon* made the jump to hyperspace. This allowed the ship to vanish and reappear somewhere far away.

When Vader's Star Destroyer spaceship was on Han Solo's tail and determined to catch him, the *Falcon*'s hyperspace drive had been damaged. Luckily, Han was an expert pilot and a quick thinker. He headed into a dangerous asteroid field, knowing that he could find a temporary hiding place there. His piloting skills allowed him to weave his ship in between the space rocks, coming to rest in an asteroid crater. Unfortunately, Han found that his hiding place wasn't actually a crater. It was the belly of an enormous space slug. Han raced his ship out of the asteroid field and landed in the only place where the *Falcon* could evade radar detection—on a tower of the Star Destroyer. His plan worked. He waited until the Star Destroyer emitted its space garbage and allowed the *Falcon* to float away with the rest of the waste. The *Millennium Falcon* had escaped undetected by the Imperial fleet.

INSIDE THE MILLENNIUM FALCON

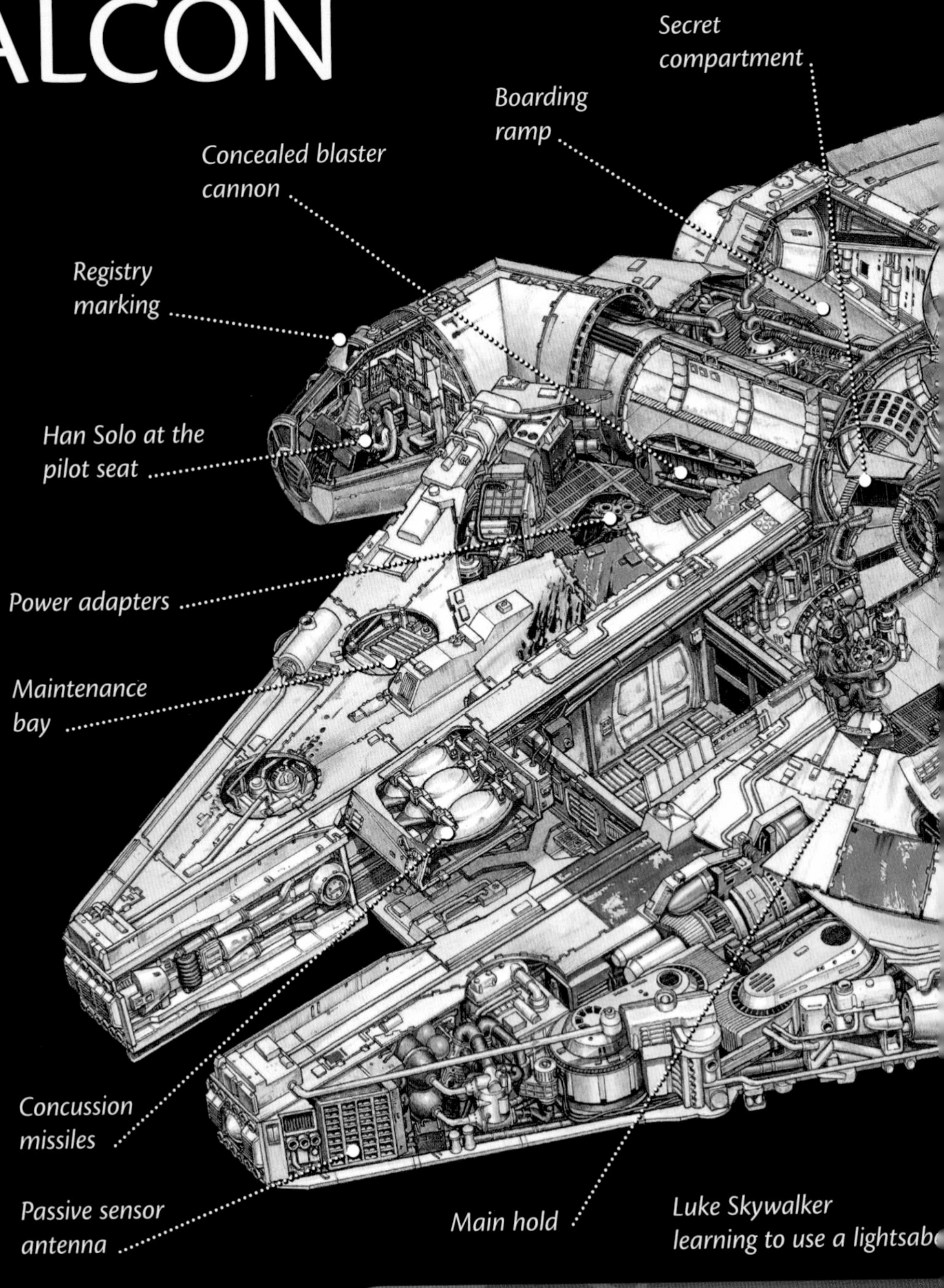

Secret compartment

Boarding ramp

Concealed blaster cannon

Registry marking

Han Solo at the pilot seat

Power adapters

Maintenance bay

Concussion missiles

Passive sensor antenna

Main hold

Luke Skywalker learning to use a lightsabe

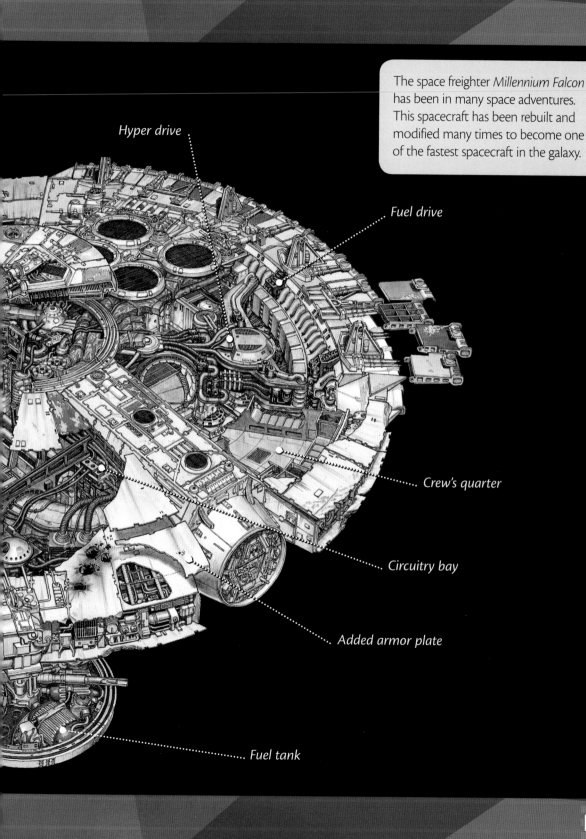

Hyper drive

Fuel drive

The space freighter *Millennium Falcon* has been in many space adventures. This spacecraft has been rebuilt and modified many times to become one of the fastest spacecraft in the galaxy.

Crew's quarter

Circuitry bay

Added armor plate

Fuel tank

THE FIRST
DEATH STAR

Darth Sidious wanted to create a physical symbol of his immense power. He ordered the construction of a huge, mobile battle station named the Death Star, which had enough firepower to destroy an entire planet.

Main power generator

Hypermatter reactor

Central computer core

DEATH STAR I

The station was the size of a moon and was divided into two hemispheres. There was a wide trench around its equator.

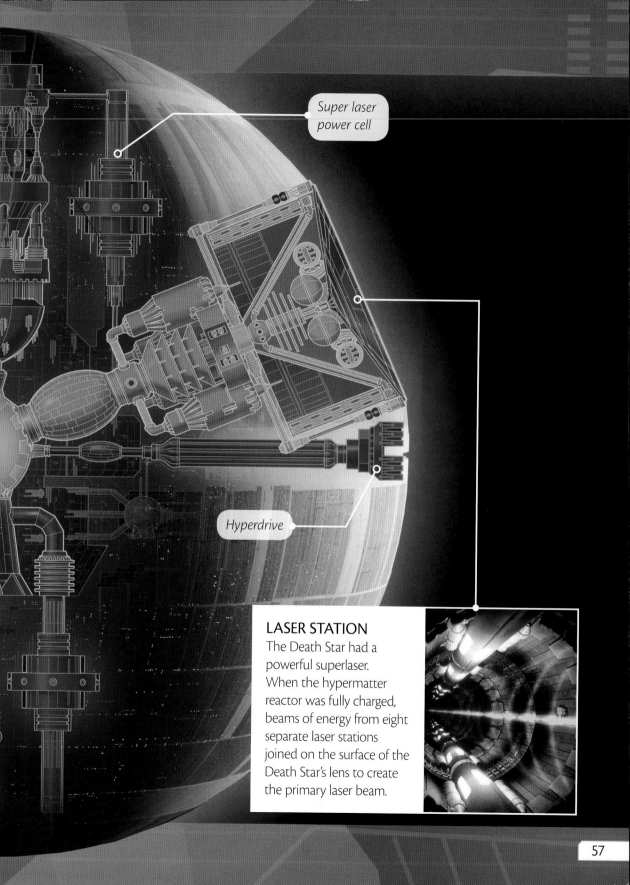

Super laser
power cell

Hyperdrive

LASER STATION
The Death Star had a
powerful superlaser.
When the hypermatter
reactor was fully charged,
beams of energy from eight
separate laser stations
joined on the surface of the
Death Star's lens to create
the primary laser beam.

Death Star Attack

The Rebel Alliance was dedicated to opposing the oppressive rule of the Galactic Empire, even though they were desperately under-equipped. The Empire had a massive starfleet, but the Alliance made do with a small number of battle-worn starfighters.

However, the rebels discovered an advantage when they stole secret plans from the Death Star. The plans revealed a flaw: If a starfighter could fire a torpedo into a tiny exhaust port, the chain reaction would destroy the entire battle station.

Rebel pilots used X-wing and Y-wing starfighters from their base on the planet Yavin 4 to launch a space assault on the Death Star.

The Empire was not expecting such small fighters to attack its deadly superweapon, and the rebel squads took advantage of this vital element of surprise. Rebel pilot Luke Skywalker was focused and skilled enough to strike the target. Chased by Imperial ships, Luke fired at the exhaust port that led into the heart of the battle station's reactor. The Death Star exploded, and the rebels scored their first major victory against the Empire.

THE SECOND DEATH STAR

The second Death Star was even bigger and more powerful than the first. Here are some of the battle station's features.

More powerful and accurate superlaser

Equatorial trench

HANGAR
The Imperial engineers allocated more hangar space in the Death Star II so it could carry more droids.

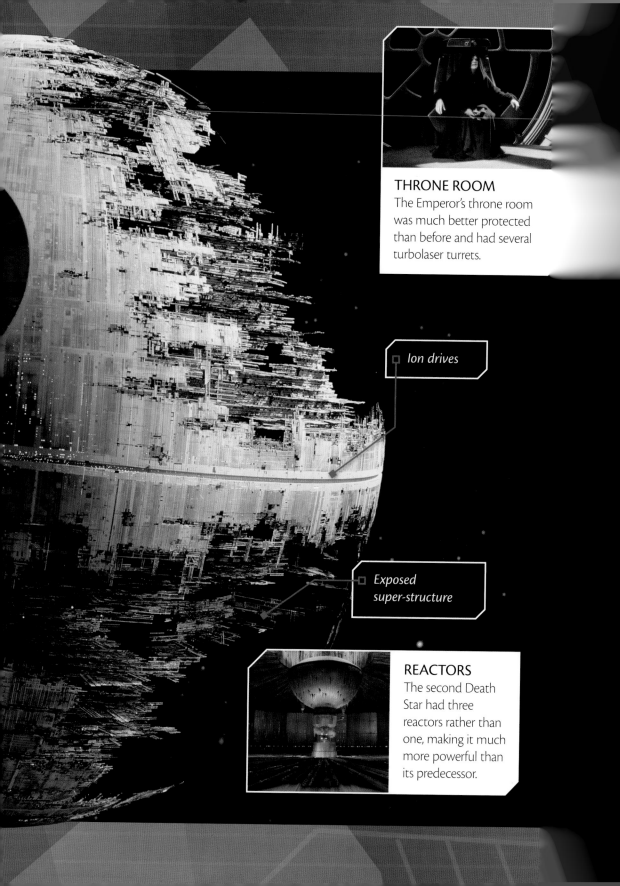

THRONE ROOM
The Emperor's throne room was much better protected than before and had several turbolaser turrets.

Ion drives

Exposed super-structure

REACTORS
The second Death Star had three reactors rather than one, making it much more powerful than its predecessor.

T-65 X-WING
STARFIGHTER

This long, narrow starship boasts excellent power, balance, and stability. After Luke Skywalker piloted his X-wing to destroy the first Death Star, it became a symbol of the Rebel Alliance.

Nose cone

Cockpit

ASTROMECH DROIDS

Like most Alliance starfighters, each X-wing has a socket for an astromech droid. They can check on flight performance, make in-flight repairs, and navigate for their pilot. The astromech droid R2-D2 helped Luke during the Battle of Yavin.

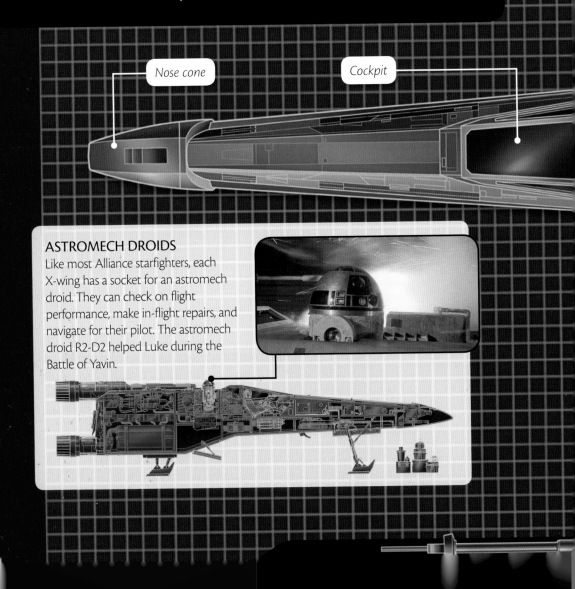

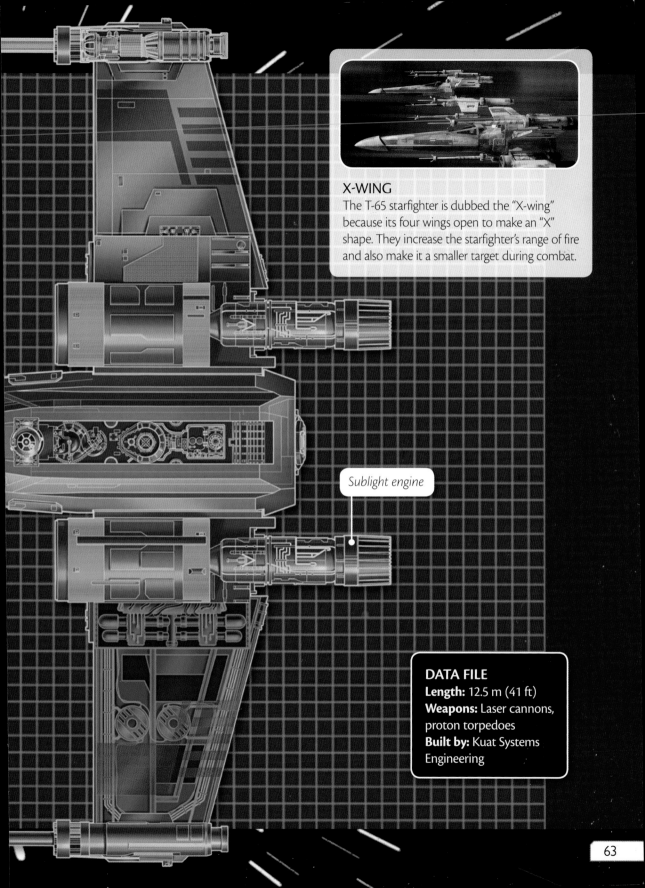

X-WING
The T-65 starfighter is dubbed the "X-wing" because its four wings open to make an "X" shape. They increase the starfighter's range of fire and also make it a smaller target during combat.

Sublight engine

DATA FILE
Length: 12.5 m (41 ft)
Weapons: Laser cannons, proton torpedoes
Built by: Kuat Systems Engineering

Final Space Battle

The last fight between the rebels and the Galactic Empire was a space battle. The entire rebel fleet came out of hiding to launch a carefully planned assault on the second Death Star.

While the rebels worked to deactivate the Death Star's energy defense shield on Endor, their fleet focused its attack on the Empire's massive Star Destroyer battleships. The rebel fleet consisted of A-wing, B-wing, and X-wing starfighters, which were able to maneuver easily around the Star Destroyers—but they were still at risk from the Death Star's deadly destroyer beam.

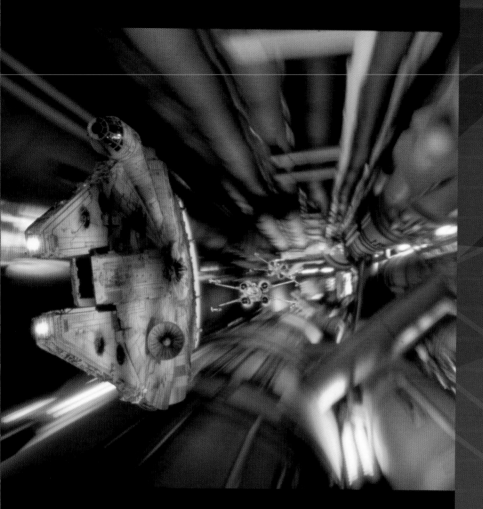

The battle turned when the rebel team on Endor succeeded in deactivating the Death Star's defense shield. A brave rebel pilot named Lando Calrissian was able to fly the *Millennium Falcon* into the Death Star's core and detonate the battle station's power plant. The resulting explosion destroyed the Death Star. The rebels had finally defeated the Galactic Empire.

LIGHTSABER CLASHES

In lightsaber combat, size doesn't matter.
Regardless of a warrior's stature, if they
have strength, dexterity, and are attuned
to the Force, they will have the power
to defeat any opponent.

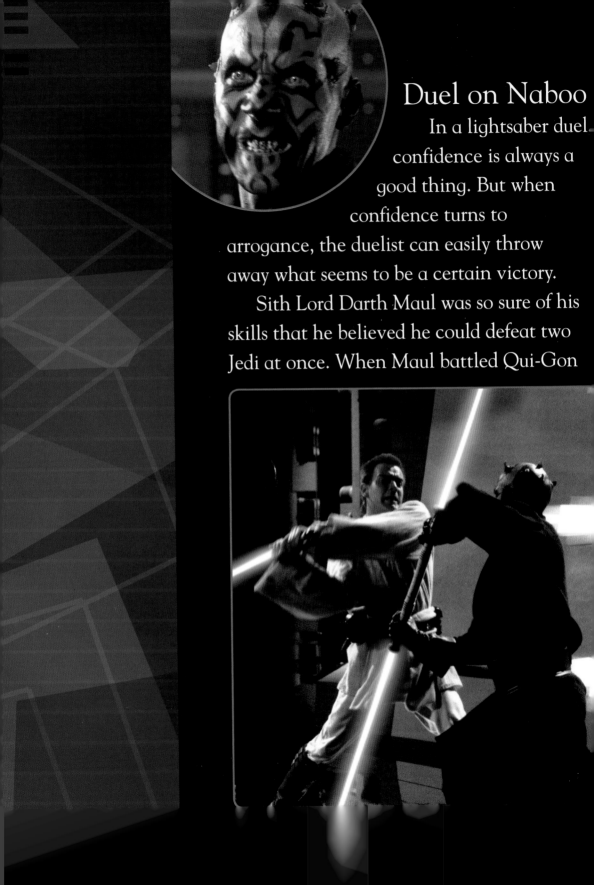

Duel on Naboo

In a lightsaber duel, confidence is always a good thing. But when confidence turns to arrogance, the duelist can easily throw away what seems to be a certain victory.

Sith Lord Darth Maul was so sure of his skills that he believed he could defeat two Jedi at once. When Maul battled Qui-Gon

Jinn and Obi-Wan Kenobi at the same time on Naboo, at first it seemed he was right. Thanks to his mastery of martial arts and his deadly saberstaff, Darth Maul was a fearsome opponent for the Jedi. Qui-Gon was fatally injured in the clash, and although Obi-Wan fought on bravely, it was clear that the Sith was more powerful.

Maul's Force push left Obi-Wan hanging from a pipe, having lost his lightsaber, and it looked as if Maul would finish off the Jedi. But his arrogance got the better of him. He stopped for a moment to taunt his opponent. Obi-Wan summoned all of his strength and used the Force to retrieve Qui-Gon's weapon, defeating Maul with one blow. Darth Maul was destroyed, a victim of his own arrogance.

HOW TO BUILD A
LIGHTSABER

Each lightsaber is made to suit its owner's needs and preferences. Lightsabers consist of a handle—called the hilt—that emits a blade of powerful energy. Special parts allow the power and length of the lightsaber blade to be changed.

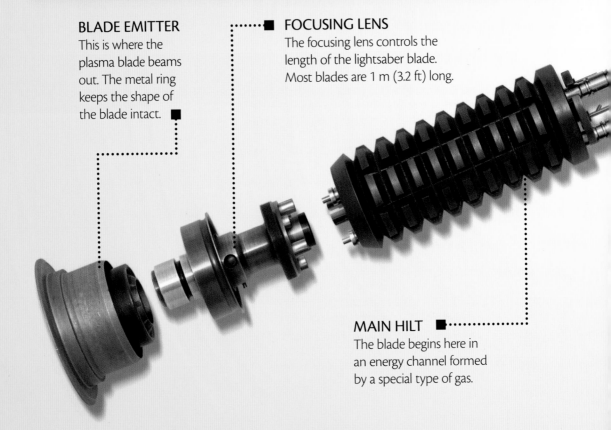

BLADE EMITTER
This is where the plasma blade beams out. The metal ring keeps the shape of the blade intact. ■

FOCUSING LENS
The focusing lens controls the length of the lightsaber blade. Most blades are 1 m (3.2 ft) long.

MAIN HILT ■
The blade begins here in an energy channel formed by a special type of gas.

CONTROLS

Buttons and switches activate the blade, but Jedi who are skilled in the Force can control the blade using the Force alone. ■

POWER CELL

Energy from special diatium batteries heats up gas to create plasma for the blade. ■

POMMEL CAP ■

The pommel seals the end of the lightsaber. It may often contain a backup battery.

Crystal

At the heart of every lightsaber hilt is a crystal that needs to be placed carefully in order to work. Jedi lightsaber crystals are mined from the planet Ilum. The Sith use artificial crystals that make their lightsabers glow red.

Duel with Dooku

The Jedi train long and hard to ensure that they always keep their cool in battle. For hotheaded young Jedi apprentice Anakin Skywalker, this skill was particularly hard to master. Anakin's impatience proved to be disastrous when he and Obi-Wan were sent to capture Sith Apprentice Count Dooku on the rocky planet of Geonosis. Dooku was once a Jedi Master but his independent spirit led him away from the order. Now he used his formidable lightsaber skills against the Jedi. As a more

experienced fighter, Obi-Wan knew that it would be better to coordinate their attack, but Anakin was too impatient to listen to his Master.

Anakin rushed toward Dooku, who used Force lightning to send Anakin crashing against a wall. Anakin's initial mistake had given the Sith Lord a great advantage. Dooku was a master swordsman who excelled in lightsaber combat and he made Anakin pay dearly for his error. In one swift blow the cruel Sith sliced off Anakin's right forearm!

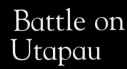

Battle on Utapau

An opponent armed with one lightsaber is a challenge for the Jedi to face. A foe armed with four lightsabers is definitely not to be underestimated! The Supreme Commander of the Separatist Army, General Grievous, was a powerful military leader until he was injured in a shuttle crash. He was rebuilt as a cyborg with four artificial arms that allowed him to wield four lightsabers at once. Despite his lightsaber training, Grievous could not use the Force like the Jedi, but his brute strength and speed made him very difficult to beat in combat.

Grievous liked to steal lightsabers from the Jedi he killed, and he hoped to add Obi-Wan's weapon to his collection!

When the two came face-to-face in one of planet Utapau's large sinkhole cities, Obi-Wan had to contend with many unpredictable attacks from the half-machine, half-creature. However, without the power of the Force, Grievous was no match for the Jedi. Obi-Wan was able to anticipate Grievous's blows and cut off several of his hands. The cyborg was forced to flee into outer space, where his tough duranium shell allowed him to withstand the crushing air pressure.

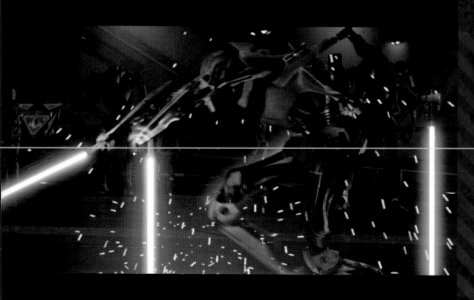

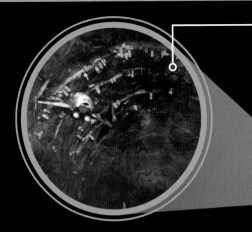

SINKHOLE
Natives live in settlements inside large sinkholes on the planet. Here, they are protected from the harsh surface winds.

PLANET SURFACE
The surface of Utapau is dry. Few plants grow here. Harsh winds sweep the planet at all times.

WELCOME TO
UTAPAU

Utapau was a peaceful planet before General Grievous and Obi-Wan's fierce battle there. Located on the Outer Rim of the galaxy, the planet and its natives had hoped to remain neutral in the battle of the Clone Wars.

Located in a large sinkhole, Pau City serves as a spaceport for visitors. It also has repair and refuelling facilities for spacecraft landing on the planet.

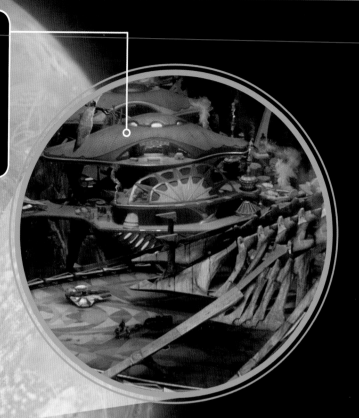

Natives

Utapau is inhabited by two native species. The tall, gray Pau'ans carry out trade and commerce. The short, stocky Utai serve as the planet's labor force.

Pau'an

Utai

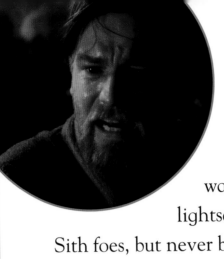

Master and Apprentice

Obi-Wan Kenobi was used to fighting fierce lightsaber duels with merciless Sith foes, but never before had he fought against a friend.

From the moment a distraught Obi-Wan learned that his Padawan, Anakin Skywalker, had become a Sith called Darth Vader, a confrontation was inevitable.

Obi-Wan faced Vader on the volcano planet of Mustafar in a dangerous lava mining facility. Obi-Wan tried to reason with him, but it was clear that Anakin had been lost to the dark side. Now transformed from friends to foes, Vader and Obi-Wan ignited their lightsabers and began an intense

battle above the flaming lava. Obi-Wan had
taught Anakin well and both fighters were
now evenly matched in strength and skill.
Having fought as a team countless times
before, the two men knew each other's
best moves—and weaknesses. In the end,
Obi-Wan's experience helped him to deal
a winning blow. Vader was defeated…
but not for long.

ANAKIN SKYWALKER: TROUBLED JEDI

THE LIGHT SIDE

Before turning to the dark side, Anakin had the potential to become a great Jedi. Many Jedi had faith in him, but he struggled to control his emotions in the way a Jedi should.

"The Force is unusually strong with him."

QUI-GON JINN

"There's something about this boy."

QUI-GON JINN

"He will not let me down."

OBI-WAN KENOBI

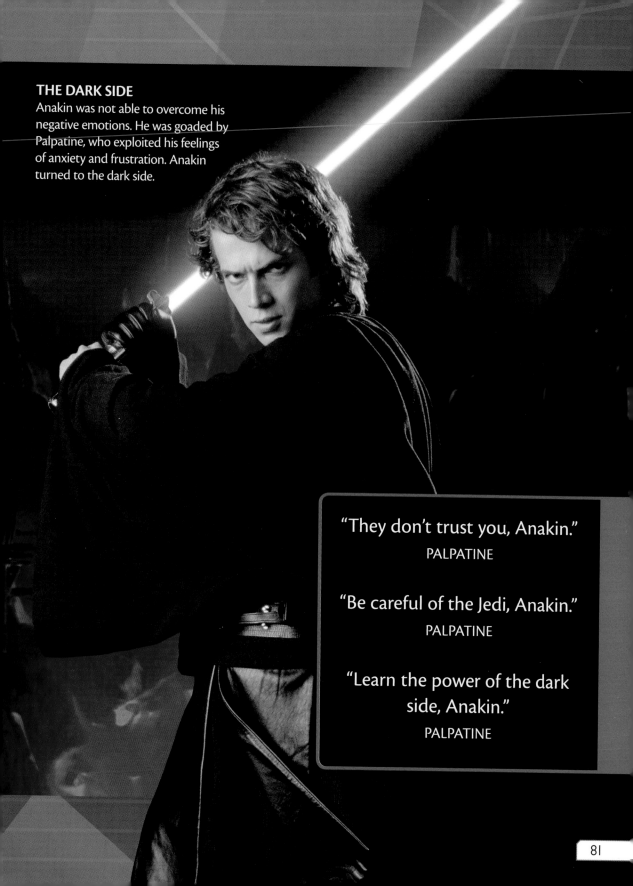

THE DARK SIDE

Anakin was not able to overcome his negative emotions. He was goaded by Palpatine, who exploited his feelings of anxiety and frustration. Anakin turned to the dark side.

"They don't trust you, Anakin."

PALPATINE

"Be careful of the Jedi, Anakin."

PALPATINE

"Learn the power of the dark side, Anakin."

PALPATINE

Close Contest

When the most powerful Jedi battled against the most powerful Sith, the two sides of the Force clashed in spectacular style. Grand Master Yoda took on Darth Sidious in the Senate building on Coruscant and proved that strength and power have nothing to do with size. The Jedi was much smaller than his Sith opponent, but he used his size and agility to his advantage. Yoda leaped and twirled above Sidious, confusing his enemy and catching

him by surprise with skillful lightsaber blows.

The devastating fury of the Sith Lord
was matched by Yoda's knowledge of the
Force, making the two equally fierce.
Using great concentration and focus,
Yoda was able to absorb Sidious's brutal
Force lightning and deflect it back again.

However, the wise old Jedi realized that
he could not defeat Sidious this time.

Yoda's size came in handy again as
he made a quick exit through a
ventilation shaft and escaped
to a distant planet
called Dagobah.

Death Star Duel

A Jedi must stay
true to the Jedi Code, no
matter how old he may be.
Obi-Wan Kenobi was an
elderly man by the time he fought against
Darth Vader once again, but his dream of
a revived Republic had not weakened.
This time their duel took place on board
the Emperor's first Death Star.

Obi-Wan Kenobi had been in hiding on Tatooine since the Emperor seized control of the galaxy. When Rebel Alliance leader Princess Leia asked for his help to take the secret Death Star plans to the Rebel Alliance, Obi-Wan recruited a young farmboy named Luke Skywalker, who knew he had latent Jedi powers. Obi-Wan knew he had to face Darth Vader again, but felt it was the only way to save Luke and Princess Leia. This duel was very different from their last. Obi-Wan was older and weaker while Vader was even stronger,

fueled by hatred and thirst for revenge. Obi-Wan knew that if he sacrificed his own life he could save his friends, so he allowed Vader to destroy him, proving to be a truly great and selfless Jedi.

MISSING
PRINCESS

Brave senator Princess Leia was taken prisoner for stealing secret plans to the Death Star. Before she was caught, she sent a message to Obi-Wan.

SECRET MESSAGE
Realizing she could not escape, Leia entrusted R2-D2 with the Death Star plans and a desperate message for Obi-Wan.

TRANSMISSION
Astromech droid R2-D2 helped fulfill his mission by transmitting Princess Leia's message through a holographic beam.

HIDDEN JEDI
Before Obi-Wan saw Leia's message he had been living in hiding. Now he needed to act immediately— he was her only hope.

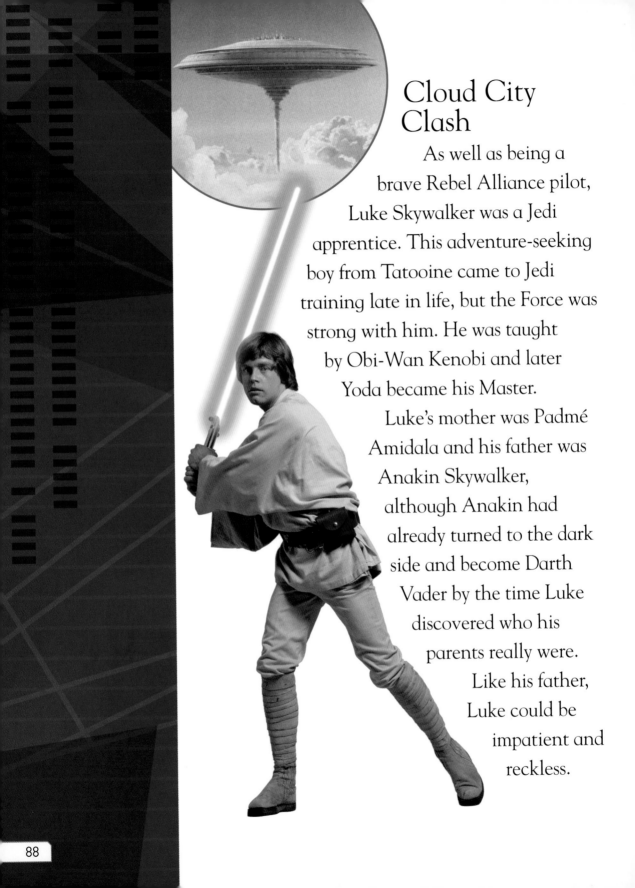

Cloud City Clash

As well as being a brave Rebel Alliance pilot, Luke Skywalker was a Jedi apprentice. This adventure-seeking boy from Tatooine came to Jedi training late in life, but the Force was strong with him. He was taught by Obi-Wan Kenobi and later Yoda became his Master.

Luke's mother was Padmé Amidala and his father was Anakin Skywalker, although Anakin had already turned to the dark side and become Darth Vader by the time Luke discovered who his parents really were. Like his father, Luke could be impatient and reckless.

Even though he had not completed his
training, Luke rushed to Cloud City where he
dueled Vader for the first time. Luke did not
yet have enough experience to combat
Vader's superior Force powers and lightsaber
skills. Vader's attack was relentless and in a
final blow, the Sith Lord severed Luke's hand.

Luke may have had many similarities to
his father but they differed in one key way:
Despite Vader's best efforts, Luke refused to be
corrupted and submit to the dark side.

Lethal Confrontation

Luke Skywalker always tried to see the good in people. He even believed that someone as cruel as his father, Darth Vader, could be saved from the dark side and never gave up hope that he could change.

Luke resisted the temptation of the dark side once again during another lightsaber duel with his father, this time on the second Death Star. Luke showed Vader that the desire for honor and justice was just as strong as the promise of incredible power, which Vader insisted the dark side would bring him.

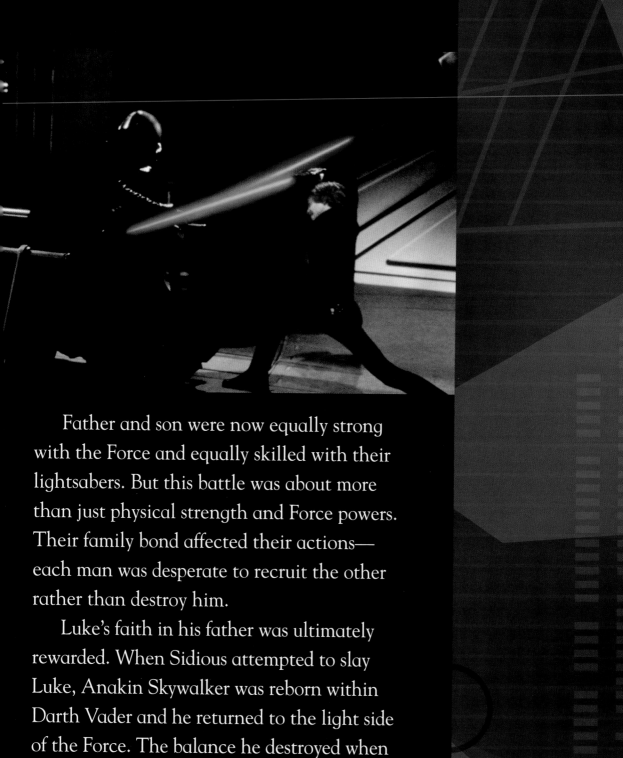

Father and son were now equally strong
with the Force and equally skilled with their
lightsabers. But this battle was about more
than just physical strength and Force powers.
Their family bond affected their actions—
each man was desperate to recruit the other
rather than destroy him.

Luke's faith in his father was ultimately
rewarded. When Sidious attempted to slay
Luke, Anakin Skywalker was reborn within
Darth Vader and he returned to the light side
of the Force. The balance he destroyed when
he became a Sith 23 years earlier was restored.

EPIC SHOWDOWNS
In the heat of conflict, combatants must rely on great daring, skill, and tactical thinking to win the day.

Kamino Conflict

In their battle for peace, the Jedi are often called upon to arrest criminals. Ten years after the victory on Naboo, Obi-Wan traveled to a watery planet called Kamino, in the hunt for a bounty hunter named Jango Fett. The Kaminoans were secretly creating a huge clone trooper army. The clone soldiers were exact copies of Jango, but they grew much faster than a human. This allowed the Kaminoans to quickly produce thousands of soldiers.

The creation of this army was supposedly ordered by a Jedi named Sifo-Dyas, but was actually done without the knowledge of the Jedi High Council, as part of Darth Sidious's master plan.

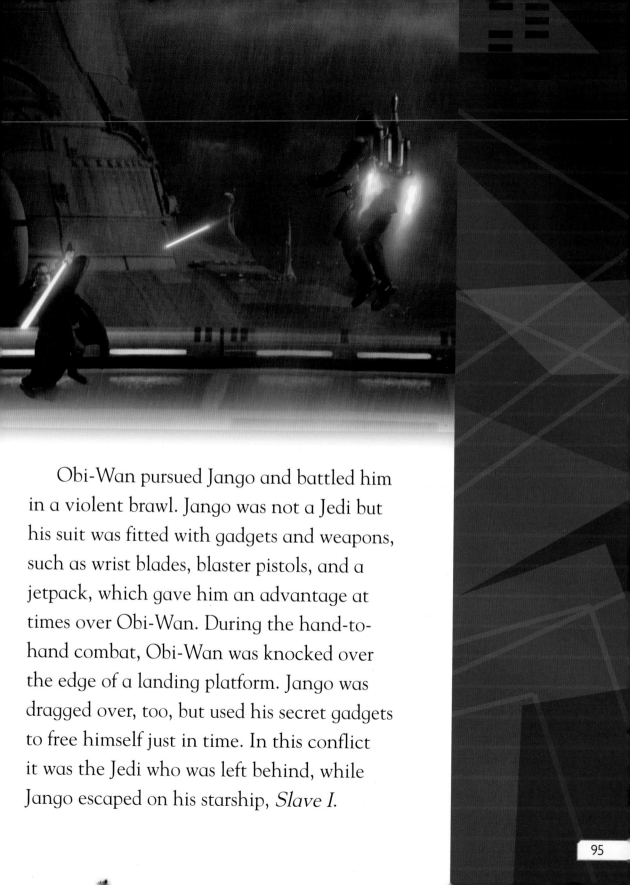

Obi-Wan pursued Jango and battled him in a violent brawl. Jango was not a Jedi but his suit was fitted with gadgets and weapons, such as wrist blades, blaster pistols, and a jetpack, which gave him an advantage at times over Obi-Wan. During the hand-to-hand combat, Obi-Wan was knocked over the edge of a landing platform. Jango was dragged over, too, but used his secret gadgets to free himself just in time. In this conflict it was the Jedi who was left behind, while Jango escaped on his starship, *Slave I*.

BOUNTY
HUNTERS

The galaxy has a thriving trade for bounty hunters like Jango Fett. These hired assassins would destroy anyone for a fee. The Sith often turned to bounty hunters to do their evil deeds.

AURRA SING

Evil Aurra left the Jedi Order to become a bounty hunter.

SPECIES: Near-human
WEAPON: Dual-triggered DX-13 blasters
SPECIALTY: Tracking prey with her sensor implants

JANGO FETT

Raised by a race of warriors, Jango was ruthless in combat.

SPECIES: Human
WEAPON: WESTAR-34 blasters
SPECIALTY: Physical combat

BOSSK

Bossk was vile and mean, and could grow back limbs lost in battle.

SPECIES: Trandoshan
WEAPON: V10 grenade launcher
SPECIALTY: Tough and merciless attitude

BOBA FETT

Boba was trained by his father, Jango Fett, and was a deadly shot.

SPECIES: Human
WEAPON: EE-3 carbine rifle
SPECIALTY: Speedy missions

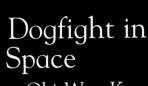

Dogfight in Space

Obi-Wan Kenobi and Jango Fett were equally tactical in battle. Their abilities were put to the test in a one-on-one dogfight deep in space.

Jango's customized spacecraft, *Slave I*, was one of the deadliest ships in the galaxy. It was armed with powerful weapons and lethal surprises. Jango's son, Boba, traveled in *Slave I* with his father, learning from his every action.

Piloting his Delta-7 starfighter, Obi-Wan chased Jango into a dangerous asteroid field. Any collision with these rocks would be fatal. Knowing this, Jango set off massive explosions that blasted rocks at the Jedi's ship. Obi-Wan may not have liked flying, but he was a skilled pilot, and he dodged each explosion. Jango's weapons were

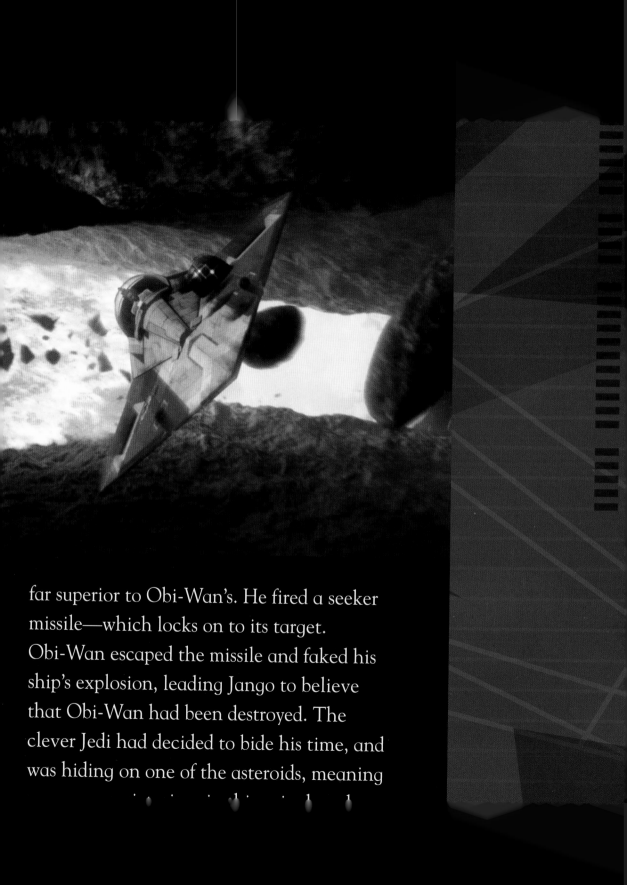

far superior to Obi-Wan's. He fired a seeker
missile—which locks on to its target.
Obi-Wan escaped the missile and faked his
ship's explosion, leading Jango to believe
that Obi-Wan had been destroyed. The
clever Jedi had decided to bide his time, and
was hiding on one of the asteroids, meaning

STARFIGHTER ESCAPE

Obi-Wan Kenobi's Delta-7 starfighter has a streamlined design, the ability to reach fast speeds, and excellent maneuverability—perfect for trying to escape a determined bounty hunter.

POWER
Equipped with two duel laser cannons, Obi-Wan's ship had the capability to unleash a withering frontal assault.

DESIGN
The sleek, blade-like form afforded excellent visibility, especially in forward and lateral directions.

COMMUNICATION
In an emergency, Kenobi's ship could relay encrypted signals in order to communicate with other Jedi.

DEFENSE
This ultra-light fighter was well shielded against impacts and blasts.

STEALTH
The tiny profile made it difficult to detect and easy to hide from long-ranged sensors.

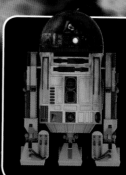

DROID HELP
An astromech droid called R4-P17 sat in the starfighter. It helped Obi-Wan escape the deadly missile.

Beastly Battle

The Jedi have faced many fearsome opponents, but none quite so gruesome and savage as the beasts on the planet Geonosis.

Obi-Wan, Anakin, and Padmé Amidala were sentenced to public execution by wild beasts in a huge arena. As Geonosians watched from the stands, three deadly creatures were let loose and set upon the human prisoners. Each one was bigger and uglier than the last! The bloodthirsty acklay walked on three pairs of giant bony claws. The reek had pointed horns on its head for goring opponents. The nexu had a mouthful of sharp

fangs that it bared in anticipation of fresh
meat. It looked like there was no way out!

However, these brutal beasts could not
triumph over the Jedi. Anakin used his Force
powers to tame the reek enough to ride it.
He charged it into the nexu, flattening it
and saving Padmé. Obi-Wan managed to
defend himself against the acklay's onslaught
long enough for the clone army to arrive,
led by Master Yoda.

GEONOSIS
ARENA BEAST

Prisoners on Geonosis were thrown into arenas with wild creatures that tried to destroy them for a crowd's entertainment. Obi-Wan Kenobi faced the vicious acklay but it was no match for the adept Jedi.

DEFENSE
Obi-Wan Kenobi used a Geonosian picador's pike to defend himself against the acklay's brutal onslaught.

DEADLY ATTACK
The acklay lives underwater, but it hunts for its prey on land. The creature has razor-sharp teeth for cutting flesh and it walks on the tips of its long claws.

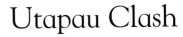

Utapau Clash

In a high-speed chase, the level of danger faced by the Jedi is even higher. On the rocky planet Utapau, Obi-Wan Kenobi would not let anything stop him from pursuing General Grievous. Their chase took them through the multilevel tunnels of Utapau's underground cities. Grievous rode his wheel bike, a deadly vehicle armed with a laser canon, while Obi-Wan rode on a varactyl lizard named Boga, which was more than capable of keeping pace with Grievous.

Obi-Wan dropped his lightsaber during the chase, but managed to grab Grievous's electrostaff. This powerful weapon emitted deadly levels of energy and was made of very strong material named phrik alloy that does not break—even after being struck by a lightsaber blade.

The enemies dueled as they rushed across Utapau's deep caverns. Grievous's heavy armor protected him from Obi-Wan's attacks, although the cyborg's armored plates became loose in their brawl.

Obi-Wan used the Force to grab Grievous's pistol and blasted his opponent through a gap in his armor. Obi-Wan's fatal shot enflamed Grievous and destroyed him in an exploding ball of fire.

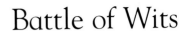

Battle of Wits

Not all battles are
a straightforward case of
pitting weaponry, skills,
and experience against the
opposing side. Quick thinking can win a
battle just as much as a superior spaceship can.

Luke Skywalker used his wits to survive
when a notorious crime lord named Jabba the
Hutt captured Princess Leia, Han Solo, and
their loyal Wookiee ally, Chewbacca.
Jabba was a slimy, gruesome gangster, but
Luke was not afraid of him and demanded
that the slug-like alien release his friends.
Jabba didn't have to physically fight Luke—

he had his own devious methods.

He dropped Luke into a rancor beast's den, but Luke's Jedi powers were so strong that he managed to trap the rancor. Jabba was not giving up yet. He ordered his guards to feed Luke and his friends to a tentacled creature named the Sarlacc. Cunningly, Luke had hidden his lightsaber inside his droid, R2-D2. R2-D2 ejected the lightsaber toward Luke who destroyed Jabba's men. Leia was quick-witted, too, and this distraction gave her the chance to strangle Jabba with her prisoner's chains. Imprisoning friends of the Jedi would be Jabba the Hutt's last mistake!

JABBA'S GANG

Crime lord Jabba the Hutt and his evil crew did not have Force powers, but they still managed to spread chaos and corruption across the galaxy.

6'0"

5'5"

5'0"

4'5"

Jabba the Hutt
Species: Hutt
Job: Crime lord

Tessek
SPECIES: Quarren
JOB: Accountant

Ephant Mon
Species: Chevin
Job: Chief of security

Bib Fortuna
Species: Twi'lek
Job: Manager of
Jabba's palace

8'5"

8'0"

7'5"

7'0"

CELEBRATION
When the people of Naboo
have something to celebrate,
such as victory in battle, they
hold a vibrant triumph parade.

A New Era

The reign of the Galactic Empire was brought to a close following the demise of Emperor Palpatine and Darth Vader, and the destruction of the second Death Star. Peace and justice were restored to the galaxy.

The good news spread quickly and people across the galaxy rejoiced. Their lives were no longer threatened.

The Rebel Alliance established a New Republic to bring democracy to the galaxy. However, the galaxy's troubles were not completely resolved.

In the future, loyal Imperial officers would continue to attack the New Republic with surviving vehicles of the

Imperial fleet, and hundreds of planets would have to be won over by the new democratic rule. At that time, however, the Emperor had been defeated; fireworks lit up the sky in celebration high above the skyscrapers of Coruscant and across many other planets, too. For Luke Skywalker, Han Solo, Princess Leia, and their friends, a new era had begun.

BATTLE ANALYSIS: NABOO

The Trade Federation, controlled by the Sith Lord Darth Sidious, invaded the planet Naboo to provoke a war. Queen Amidala and her allies led six dangerous missions to put an end to the invasion.

1. GRASS PLAINS

OBJECTIVE:
Gungans to create a diversion for the droid army.

OUTCOME:
Battle begins, droids are successfully distracted.

MISSION COMPLETE

2. THEED PALACE

OBJECTIVE:
Queen Amidala and her soldiers to sneak into the royal palace.

OUTCOME:
Team avoids battle droids and enters through window.

MISSION COMPLETE

3. SPACE BATTLE

OBJECTIVE:
Naboo starfighter pilots to destroy the Droid Control Ship.

....

OUTCOME:
Pilots engage hostile vulture droids, but suffer losses.

MISSION FAILED

4. JEDI VS. SITH DUEL

OBJECTIVE:
Jedi to eliminate the Sith Darth Maul.

....

OUTCOME:
Obi-Wan defeats Maul, but Qui-Gon dies.

MISSION COMPLETE

5. THEED THRONE ROOM

OBJECTIVE:
Queen Amidala to capture the Trade Federation viceroy, Nute Gunray.

....

OUTCOME:
Queen outsmarts the viceroy and makes him surrender.

MISSION COMPLETE

6. DROID CONTROL SHIP DESTRUCTION

MISSION COMPLETE

OBJECTIVE:
Naboo pilots to destroy the Droid Control Ship.

OUTCOME:
Anakin Skywalker blows up the ship, shutting down the droid army.

BATTLE ANALYSIS: GEONOSIS

The Separatists—led by Count Dooku—built a large droid army. When Obi-Wan Kenobi was captured by Count Dooku, the Republic sent envoys and troops to Geonosis to resolve the issue.

 1. **DROID FACTORY**

OBJECTIVE:
Anakin Skywalker and Padmé Amidala to rescue Obi-Wan Kenobi.

OUTCOME:
Anakin Skywalker and Padmé Amidala are captured.

MISSION FAILED

2. **EXECUTION ARENA**

OBJECTIVE:
Anakin, Padmé, and Obi-Wan to escape execution.

OUTCOME:
Captives survive and destroy vicious beasts.

MISSION COMPLETE

3. JEDI STRIKE FORCE

OBJECTIVE:
Jedi team to rescue cap[tured]
droids.

OUTCOME:
Many Jedi killed, Jedi su[rvivors]
surrounded by droid ar[my]

MISSION INCOMP[LETE]

4. ARRIVAL OF CLONE ARMY

OBJECTIVE:
Clone army to rescue survivors.

OUTCOME:
Survivors airlifted out of arena.

MISSION COMPLETE

5. BATTLE OF GEONOSIS

OBJECTIVE:
Jedi to lead clone troopers and
vehicles against droid army.

OUTCOME:
Despite many fatalities during a full-
scale battle, clone army is victorious.

MISSION COMPLETE

6. DUEL WITH DOOKU

OBJECTIVE:
Obi-Wan, Anakin, and Yoda
to prevent Count Dooku's
escape from Geonosis.

OUTCO[ME]
Anakin l[oses]
arm, Co[unt]
Dooku e[scapes]

MISSION FAILED

BATTLE ANALYSI
YAVIN

The Emperor's Death Star tracked the rebels to their headquarters on Yavin 4. The Rebel Alliance only had one chance to destroy the powerful battle station and save themselves.

1. DEATH STAR APPROACH

OBJECTIVE:
Red and Gold Squadrons to weaken the Death Star's defenses.

OUTCOME:
The Death Star's ion cannons and communications centers are taken out.

MISSION COMPLETE

2. SPACE BATTLE

OBJECTIVE:
Rebel pilots to wipe out Imperial TIE fighters.

OUTCOME:
During fast-paced combat both sides take losses.

MISSION FAILED

3. FIRST TRENCH RUN

OBJECTIVE:
Gold Squadron's Y-wings to hit the Death Star's thermal exhaust port.

OUTCOME:
Y-wings destroyed by Darth Vader.

MISSION FAILED

4. SECOND TRENCH RUN

OBJECTIVE:
Red Squadron's X-wings to hit the thermal exhaust port.

OUTCOME:
X-wings fire but miss, and are destroyed by Darth Vader.

MISSION FAILED

5. DARTH VADER

OBJECTIVE:
Millennium Falcon to attack Darth Vader.

OUTCOME:
Han Solo damages Vader's special TIE fighter, so Luke can fire at the Death Star's exhaust port.

MISSION COMPLETE

6. FINAL CHANCE

OBJECTIVE:
Luke Skywalker to destroy the Death Star.

OUTCOME:
Luke torpedoes the exhaust port, blowing up the Death Star.

MISSION COMPLETE

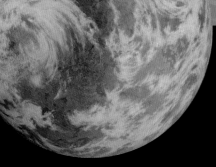

BATTLE ANALYSIS: ENDOR

The Rebel Alliance was on a mission to shut down the second Death Star. A strike team landed on Endor to demolish it. This report examines the events of the Battle on Endor.

1. CAPTURED

OBJECTIVE:
Han Solo, Princess Leia, and Chewbacca to destroy the shield generator.

....

OUTCOME:
The trio realizes they have walked into a trap and are captured.

MISSION FAILED

2. SPACE BATTLE

OBJECTIVE:
Rebels to elude Imperial warships near the Death Star.

OUTCOME:
Rebels destroy Imperial ships, but take heavy losses, too.

MISSION INCOMPLETE

3. LAND BATTLE

OBJECTIVE:
Rebels to fight their way out of the Imperial trap.

....

OUTCOME:
Ewoks join the fight and beat the soldiers with spears and rocks.

MISSION COMPLETE

4. DEATH STAR DUEL

OBJECTIVE:
Luke Skywalker to defeat the Emperor.

....

OUTCOME:
Darth Vader throws the Emperor into a shaft to save Luke.

MISSION COMPLE

5. SHIELD GENERATOR

OBJECTIVE:
Strike team to destroy the shield protecting the Death Star.

....

OUTCOME:
This time, the generator is blown up.

6. DESTROY DEATH STAR

OBJECTIVE:
Lando to trigger an explosion in the Death Star's main reactor.

OUTCOME:
With the shield down, Lando blasts the core.

MISSION COMPLETE

MISSION COMPLETE

Quiz

1. What was Yoda's rank in the Jedi Order?

2. The Trade Federation was run by which greedy aliens?

3. What power source is housed in the hilt of a Jedi's lightsaber?

4. How many members of the Jedi High Council were there?

5. Which brave pilot destroyed the Droid Control Ship?

6. Where did the land battle between the Gungan army and the Trade Federation army occur?

7. Which Jedi is said to have ordered the creation of a secret clone army?

8. To which planet did Yoda flee after his fight with Count Dooku?

9. What type of rifle did Boba Fett carry?

10. What was the length of a vulture droid?

11. The Rebel Alliance launched a space assault on the first Death Star from their base on which planet?

12. Where did Leia hide her message for Obi-Wan?

13. What type of beast did Luke Skywalker defeat inside Jabba's palace?

14. How many reactors were there on the second Death Star?

15. Which furry creatures helped the Rebel Alliance on the forest moon of Endor?

Glossary

Apprentice
A trainee.

Bounty hunter
Someone who searches for and captures people for a reward.

Chancellor
The person who leads the government, known as the Senate.

Chasm
A deep hole.

Clone
An exact copy of something or someone.

Clone Wars
The conflict between the Republic and the Separatists.

Compassion
Sympathy for others.

Corporation
A group of businesses that have formed an organization.

Cyborg
Someone who is part-living and part-robot.

Death Star
A battle station and superweapon developed by the Empire.

Deflect
To block something coming toward you and force it in another direction or back at an opponent.

Divert
To change the direction of something.

Droid
A type of robot.

Empire
A group of nations or worlds ruled by one leader—the Emperor.

Extinct
Something that has died out.

Galaxy
A group of millions of stars and planets.

Gloat
To be smug about something.

Goad
To deliberately anger and irritate someone.

Grand Master
The head of the Jedi Order.

Jedi High Council
The governing body of the Jedi Order.

Jedi Order
A group of beings who defend peace and justice in the galaxy.

Lightsaber
A sword-like weapon with a blade made of pure energy. It is used by the Jedi and Sith.

Manipulate
To control or influence someone.

Reactor
A device in spaceships used to generate power for travel.

Quiz answers
1. Jedi Grand Master
2. Neimoidians 3. A crystal
4. 12 5. Anakin Skywalker
6. Great Grass Plains of Naboo
7. Jedi Master Sifo-Dyas
8. Dagobah 9. EE-3 carbine rifle
10. 6.96 m (22.75 ft) 11. Inside
R2-D2 12. *Tantive IV*
13. A rancor 14. Three
15. Ewoks

Rebel Alliance
A group who want to overthrow the Empire.

Repel
To force something back.

Republic
A nation, world, or group of worlds in which people vote for their leaders.

Senator
An elected representative of the government.

Separatists
Those who oppose the Galactic Republic.

Sinkhole
A hole in the rock beneath a planet's surface.

Sith
Evil beings who use the dark side of the Force.

Underestimate
To not value someone's abilities highly enough.

Viceroy
An official who is a representative of the Emperor.

Wield
To handle a weapon or tool.

127

STAR WARS

CHARACTER PROFILES

WRITTEN BY
SIMON BEECROFT AND PABLO HIDALGO

AAYLA SECURA

TWI'LEK JEDI KNIGHT

DATA FILE

AFFILIATION: Jedi
HOMEWORLD: Ryloth
SPECIES: Twi'lek
HEIGHT: 1.7m (5ft 7in)
APPEARANCES: II, CW, III
SEE ALSO: Yoda

Has mastered Ataru, Form IV of lightsaber combat

Lekku (head-tail)

Djem So attack stance

Belt made of rycrit hide

Fitted clothing allows complete freedom of movement

CUNNING AAYLA SECURA

is a Twi'lek Jedi Knight who relies on her athletic lightsaber skills to outwit opponents. As a Jedi General, Aayla leads a squad of clone troopers on many campaigns.

AAYLA SECURA is an intelligent, sometimes mischievous Jedi. Her teacher was a troubled Jedi named Quinlan Vos. Aayla passes on the teachings of her Master to young Ahsoka Tano during a Clone Wars mission that goes awry and ends up on the grassland planet of Maridun.

Captured

At the Battle of Geonosis, Aayla Secura is among the circle of Jedi captured by Geonosian soldiers. Luckily, clone trooper reinforcements come to their rescue.

Secura's own clone troopers turn on her on Felucia.

ANAKIN SKYWALKER

LEGENDARY JEDI KNIGHT

Gauntlet covers mechno-hand (which replaces hand sliced off by Count Dooku)

Jedi utility belt

DATA FILE

AFFILIATION: Podracing, Jedi, Sith
HOMEWORLD: Tatooine
SPECIES: Human
HEIGHT: 1.85m (6ft 1in)
APPEARANCES: I, II, CW, III, VI
SEE ALSO: Qui-Gon Jinn; Obi-Wan Kenobi; Padmé Amidala

Young Anakin's keen perception and unnaturally fast reflexes show his great Force potential.

IN THE CLONE WARS, Anakin loses his faith in the Jedi to restore peace and harmony to the galaxy. He also feels great anger at the tragic death of his mother and fears that the same fate may befall Padmé Amidala (who is secretly his wife). Finally, Anakin is persuaded that only the dark side can give him the power to prevent death.

ANAKIN SKYWALKER'S ise to power is astonishing. n a few short years, he goes rom being a slave on atooine to becoming one f the most powerful Jedi ver. But Anakin's thirst for ower leads him to the dark ide of the Force, with tragic onsequences for the galaxy.

nakin's impulsive nature leads m toward the dark side.

Close Bond

Anakin's bond with his teacher, Obi-Wan Kenobi, is strong. They make a dynamic team in the Clone Wars, where Anakin proves to be a great leader. Yet Anakin is troubled by feelings of anger and mistrust.

AURRA SING

VICIOUS BOUNTY HUNTER

DATA FILE

AFFILIATION: Bounty hunter
HOMEWORLD: Nar Shaddaa
SPECIES: Human
HEIGHT: 1.83m (6ft)
APPEARANCES: I, CW
SEE ALSO: Bossk; Padmé
Amidala; Boba Fett

AURRA SING is a ruthless bounty hunter. A seemingly ageless veteran of the underworld scene, Aurra worked with such contemporaries as Jango Fett, and Cad Bane. During the Clone Wars, she was hired by Ziro the Hutt to assassinate Padmé Amidala.

Tracker
utility vest

Short-
range pistol

Long fingers
to draw blood

AURRA SING was born in the polluted urban sprawl of Nar Shaddaa. She never knew her father and her mother was too poor to raise her. Sing became a cold-blooded killer. She is willing to use any means necessary to locate her prey. She has sensor implants and has a wide assortment of weapons in her private arsenal, including lightsabers and a sniper's projectile rifle.

Long-range
projectile rifle

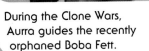

During the Clone Wars, Aurra guides the recently orphaned Boba Fett.

High Alert

On the trail of her quarry on Tatooine, Aurra Sing is a spectator at the Podrace that will earn young Anakin Skywalker his freedom.

BIB FORTUNA

JABBA'S TWI'LEK MAJOR-DOMO

DATA FILE

AFFILIATION: Jabba's court
HOMEWORLD: Ryloth
SPECIES: Twi'lek
HEIGHT: 2m (6ft 7in)
APPEARANCES: I, VI
SEE ALSO: Jabba the Hutt

THE SINISTER BIB FORTUNA

oversees the day-to-day affairs of Jabba the Hutt's desert palace and his estate in Mos Eisley. Before working with Jabba, Bib Fortuna became rich as a slave trader of his own people, the Twi'leks.

Lekku (head-tails; one of two)

Fortuna hovers near Jabba's ear, whispering advice. Secretly, he plots to kill Jabba!

Silver bracelet

Traditional Ryloth robe

Tricked

Bib Fortuna has been Jabba's major-domo (head of staff) for many decades. When two droids arrive unexpectedly to bargain for Han Solo's life, Fortuna unwittingly kickstarts a chain of events that leads to the downfall of the notorious Hutt gangster.

Soft-soled shoes for silent creeping

BIB FORTUNA is a powerful and dreaded individual in Jabba's entourage. Whether you are a friend or a foe, Fortuna will use underhand means against you in order to maintain his control within the organization.

133

BOBA FETT

THE BEST BOUNTY HUNTER IN THE GALAXY

DATA FILE

AFFILIATION: Bounty hunter
HOMEWORLD: Kamino
SPECIES: Human clone
HEIGHT: 1.83m (6ft)
APPEARANCES: II, CW, IV, V, VI
SEE ALSO: Jango Fett;
Darth Vader; Han Solo;
Jabba the Hutt

COOL AND CALCULATING, Boba Fett is a legendary bounty hunter. He is paid to track down and, often, kill targeted individuals. Over the years, Fett has developed a code of honor, and only accepts missions which meet this harsh sense of justice.

Multifunction helmet

EE-3 blaster rifle

Reinforced flight suit

Utility belt

On his first mission for Vader, Boba unwittingly reveals that Vader's son is alive by discovering that a Skywalker destroyed the Death Star.

BOBA FETT'S talent and skill, combined with an arsenal of exotic weapons, has brought in many "impossible" bounties. He is notorious for completely disintegrating those whom he has been hired to track down.

Like Father, Like Son

Boba Fett is an exact genetic clone of Jango Fett, who brings Boba up as a son. Boba witnesses Jango's death at the Battle of Geonosis and swears revenge against the Jedi who killed him. In time, he inherits Jango Fett's Mandalorian battle armor and his ship, *Slave I*.

Working for Darth Vader, Fett captures Han Solo and loads his carbon-frozen body into *Slave I*.

BOSS NASS

GUNGAN LEADER

DATA FILE

AFFILIATION: Gungan Rep Council, Gungan Grand Army
HOMEWORLD: Naboo
SPECIES: Gungan
HEIGHT: 2.06m (6ft 9in)
APPEARANCES: I, III
SEE ALSO: Padmé Amidala; Jar Jar Binks

Crown of rulership

Epaulets of military authority

Four-fingered hand

The Gungan High Council has the power to summon the Gungan Grand Army.

BOSS NASS sits on the Gungan High Council. He is a fair but stubborn ruler. He particularly resents the Naboo's belief that the Gungans are primitive simply because Gungans prefer to use traditional crafts and technologies.

Long coat with golden clasp

BOSS NASS is the stern, old-fashioned ruler of Otoh Gunga, the largest of the Gungan underwater cities on Naboo. He speaks Galactic Basic (the most widely used language in the galaxy) with a strong accent.

or Jar Jar's help during the Naboo blockade, Nass reverses is banishment from Otoh Gunga.

Teamwork

When his planet is faced with invasion, Boss Nass puts aside his prejudice against the Naboo. He receives Queen Amidala when she humbly asks him for help. Boss Nass realizes that his people must work together with the Naboo or die, and a new friendship is forged between the two cultures.

135

BOSSK

TRANDOSHAN BOUNTY HUNTER

DATA FILE

AFFILIATION: Bounty hunter
HOMEWORLD: Trandosha
SPECIES: Trandoshan
HEIGHT: 1.9m (6ft 3in)
APPEARANCES: CW, V, VI
SEE ALSO: Aurra Sing;
Boba Fett; Darth Vader

Eyes can see in infrared range

THE TOUGH AND RESILIENT Bossk is a reptilian Trandoshan bounty hunter. He used to track runaway slaves. Now he claims bounties for the Empire, and is incredibly successful at capturing his prey.

Sling for grenade launcher

Flak vest

Relby v-10 micro grenade launcher

BOSSK began his career doing a form of bounty hunting that few other species would risk: hunting Wookiees. Later, he hunts other species. During the Clone Wars, Bossk teams up with Aurra Sing, young Boba Fett, and a Klatooinian bounty hunter named Castas.

Lost fingers, skin, and even limbs can regrow until adulthood

Bossk and other bounty hunters frequently visit Jabba the Hutt, seeking their next job.

Tough Trandoshan

Fond of skinning his captives when possible, Bossk is as vile and mean as bounty hunters get. He is one of the six bounty hunters Darth Vader enlists to track down and capture the *Millennium Falcon*.

C-3PO

GOLDEN PROTOCOL DROID

DATA FILE

AFFILIATION: Republic/
Rebel Alliance/Resistance
TYPE: Protocol droid
MANUFACTURER: Cybot
Galactica
HEIGHT: 1.67m (5ft 6in)
APPEARANCES: I, II, CW, III,
R, IV, V, VI, VII
SEE ALSO: R2-D2;
Anakin Skywalker;
Luke Skywalker

Vocabulator

Primary power
coupling outlet

Replacement arm
from another droid

Reinforced knee joint

C-3PO IS PROGRAMMED
to assist in matters of etiquette
and translation. Thrown into
a world of adventure, he is
often overwhelmed by the
action around him. But he
forms a capable team
when partnered with
the resourceful R2-D2.

Anakin Skywalker built
the working skeleton of
C-3PO from scrap parts.

Golden God

Despite his fear of excitement, C-3PO has
led an adventurous life, often losing limbs
or bits of circuitry along the way (though
he is easily repaired). On Endor, a tribe
of Ewoks worships C-3PO as a "golden
god," which leads the Ewoks to support
the rebels and play a decisive role in
defeating the Empire.

C-3PO first works for Anakin
Skywalker and his mother, Shmi. Anakin
then gives C-3PO to Senator Padmé
Amidala as a wedding gift. After
Padmé's death, C-3PO is assigned to
Bail Organa, until Darth Vader captures
the *Tantive IV*. C-3PO escapes to
Tatooine and is sold to Luke Skywalker.

CHEWBACCA

WOOKIEE WARRIOR, PILOT, AND HERO

DATA FILE

AFFILIATION: Rebel
Alliance/Resistance
HOMEWORLD: Kashyyyk
SPECIES: Wookiee
HEIGHT: 2.28m (7ft 6in)
APPEARANCES: CW, III,
IV, V, VI, VII
SEE ALSO: Han Solo;
Tarfful

CHEWBACCA is a Wookiee mechanic and pilot. During the Clone Wars, he fights to defend his planet. In the time of the Empire, he is first mate and loyal friend to Han Solo aboard the *Millennium Falcon*.

CHEWIE SERVES

as Han Solo's fiercely loyal copilot and trusty fellow adventurer. He enjoys the thrilling action that Solo gets them into, but sometimes tries to act as a check on his partner's willfulness.

Bowcaster

Water-shedding hair

Tool pouch

Thirty years after the Rebellion, Han and Chewie are still side by side.

Wookiee Mechanic

The great Wookiee uses his mechanical abilities to keep Solo's starship flying. Later, he will employ these skills to completely reconstruct C-3PO after the poor droid is blasted apart on Cloud City.

COUNT DOOKU

SEPARATIST LEADER AND SITH LORD

DATA FILE

AFFILIATION: Sith, Separatists
HOMEWORLD: Serenno
SPECIES: Human
HEIGHT: 1.93m (6ft 4in)
APPEARANCES: II, CW, III
SEE ALSO: Palpatine;
Anakin Skywalker

Cape is
emblem
of Count of
Serenno

Caught between Anakin's blades, Dooku
is unprepared for Sidious's treachery.

COUNT DOOKU was
once a Jedi Master. But
his independent spirit led
him away from the Order
and he became a Sith
apprentice, named Darth
Tyranus. As Dooku, he
leads the Separatist
movement, which
seeks independence
from the Republic.

Curved
lightsaber

COUNT DOOKU

is a member of the nobility on his
homeworld of Serenno, and one
of the richest men in the galaxy.
He uses his wealth and power
to convince many star systems
to join his Separatist movement.

Boots of
rare rancor
leather

During the first battle of
Geonosis, Dooku fights
Yoda—his former master.

Sith Skills

Count Dooku is a formidable opponent.
He is a master of ancient Form II lightsaber
combat, characterized by graceful moves.
He can also project deadly streams of
Sith Force lightning from his fingertips.

DARTH MAUL

SITH SURVIVOR

DATA FILE

AFFILIATION: Sith, Nightbrothers
HOMEWORLD: Dathomir
SPECIES: Zabrak
HEIGHT: 1.75m (5ft 9in)
APPEARANCES: I, CW
SEE ALSO: Qui-Gon Jinn; Obi-Wan Kenobi; Palpatine

Face markings

Field cloak

Maul meets with his Sith Master, Darth Sidious.

DARTH MAUL IS Darth Sidious's apprentice and one of the most dangerous and highly trained Sith in the history of the Order. His entire body is marked with patterns that show his heritage as a part of the warrior tribe known as the Nightbrothers of Dathomir.

Lightsaber blade is red due to nature of internal crystals

Heavy-action boots

Maul Versus Keno

Sent to capture Queen Amidala durin the invasion of Naboo, Maul gives Je Master Qui-Gon Jinn and Obi-Wan Kenobi the rare opportunity to fight a trained Sith warrior. Jinn first duels with Maul on Tatooine. He faces M a second time on Naboo, this time with Kenobi. Kenobi thought he ha destroyed the evil Sith, but Maul survived the devastating wound.

DARTH MAUL was believed dead by the Jedi, but his lust for vengeance kept him alive. Reanimated by Nightsister magicks, Maul returned during the Clone Wars to wreak havoc in th criminal underworld before being captured by Darth Sidious. Maul once again narrowly escaped death.

DARTH VADER

DARK LORD OF THE SITH

DATA FILE

AFFILIATION: Sith
HOMEWORLD: Tatooine
SPECIES: Human
HEIGHT: (armored) 2.02m
(6ft 7in)
APPEARANCES: III, R, IV,
V, VI
SEE ALSO: Palpatine;
Luke Skywalker

Darth Vader fights the battle that
will result in his encasement
in a life-support suit.

THE GRIM, FORBIDDING
figure of Darth Vader is
Emperor Palpatine's
Sith apprentice and a
much-feared military
commander. Vader's
knowledge of the
dark side of the Force
makes him unnerving
and dangerous.

Control function panel

AFTER VADER'S
near-fatal duel with
Obi-Wan Kenobi on
Mustafar, Palpatine has
his apprentice encased
in black armor. Vader
is unable to survive
without the constant life
support provided
by his black suit.

Sith blade

Outer cloak

Palpatine is pleased with his
apprentice's terrifying new form.

Father and Son

When Vader learns that Luke Skywalker is his son, he
harbors a desire to turn Luke to the dark side and
rule the galaxy with him. Yet Luke refuses to lose
sight of Vader's humanity under the armor.

GENERAL GRIEVOUS

COMMANDER OF THE DROID ARMY

DATA FILE

AFFILIATION: Separatists
HOMEWORLD: Kalee
SPECIES: Kaleesh (cyborg)
HEIGHT: 2.16m (7ft 1in)
APPEARANCES: CW, III
SEE ALSO: Count Dooku;
Palpatine; Obi-Wan Kenobi

GENERAL GRIEVOUS is the Supreme Commander of the Droid Army during the Clone Wars. Grievous reacts furiously to any suggestion that he is a droid. In fact, he is a cyborg: a twisted mix of organic body parts and mechanical armor, with a hunched back and a bad cough.

Grievous's end comes when Obi-Wan Kenobi fires blaster bolts at his vulnerable gutsack.

GRIEVOUS IS a Kaleesh warlord who was rebuilt to increase his fighting prowess. The cyborg general is not Force-sensitive, but Darth Tyranus (Count Dooku) trained him in lightsaber combat.

Reptilian eyes

Cape contains pockets for lightsabers

Electro-driven arms can split in half

Grievous makes a daring assault on Coruscant in his flagship—the *Invisible Hand*.

Prepared for Battle

After their battle during the rescue of Palpatine, Obi-Wan Kenobi faces Grievous again in the Separatist base on Utapau. This time Grievous splits apart his arms in order to wield four lightsabers.

HAN SOLO

SMUGGLER AND WAR HERO

DATA FILE

AFFILIATION: Rebel Alliance/
Resistance
HOMEWORLD: Corellia
SPECIES: Human
HEIGHT: 1.8m (5ft 11in)
APPEARANCES: IV, V, VI, VII
SEE ALSO: Chewbacca;
Princess Leia

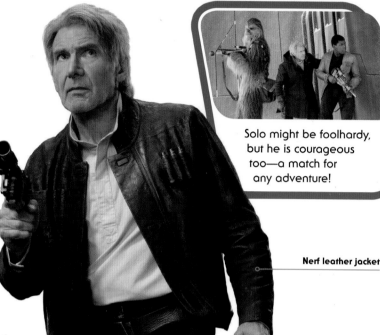

Solo might be foolhardy,
but he is courageous
too—a match for
any adventure!

Nerf leather jacket

AN SOLO IS A pirate,
muggler, and mercenary. With
is loyal first mate, Chewbacca,
e flies one of the fastest ships in the
alaxy—the *Millennium Falcon*. Han is
eckless at times, but he proves himself
natural leader in the Rebel Alliance.

CHANGE is a constant
in Solo's life. As a young man,
he believed he made his own
luck and was a man of few
responsibilities. As he grows
older and wiser, he has difficulty
settling down to a life of peace.
After suffering personal
tragedy, Han once again
returns to a reckless life in
the criminal underworld.

Action boots

trike Force

n Solo leads a group of rebels, including
ewbacca and Leia, in a risky mission on Endor's
on to destroy the second Death Star's shield
nerator. Solo shows Leia that there is more to
ng a scoundrel than having a checkered past!

143

JABBA THE HUTT

NOTORIOUS CRIME LORD

DATA FILE

AFFILIATION: Grand Hutt Council, Crymorah Syndicate
HOMEWORLD: Tatooine
SPECIES: Hutt
LENGTH: 3.9m (12ft 10in)
APPEARANCES: I, CW, IV, VI
SEE ALSO: Bib Fortuna

THE REPELLENT CRIME LORD Jabba the Hutt commands an extensive criminal empire. He built his operation through a long history of deals, threats, extortion, murders, and good business sense. Now, Jabba lives a life of wickedness in his palace located on the remote desert world of Tatooine.

Hutt skin secretes oil and mucus

Muscular body can move like a snail

Princess Leia exacts the revenge that all Jabba's slaves have dreamed abou

Body ho no skeleto

Ruler

Sitting on his throne, with his slaves and sycophants all around, Jabba presides over a court of murderous depravity. Many bounty hunters and hired thugs seek work here.

JABBA REIGNS as head of the Hutt Grand Council, one of the largest criminal empires in the galaxy. Jabba prefers Tatooine to Nal Hutta, so Gardulla the Hutt often serves as his representative on the council. During the Clone Wars, Jabba allows the Republic to use private Hutt hyperspace lanes in exchange for rescuing his son, Rotta, from kidnappers.

JANGO FETT

DATA FILE

AFFILIATION: Bounty hunter, Separatists

HOMEWORLD: Unknown

SPECIES: Human

HEIGHT: 1.83m (6ft)

APPEARANCES: II

SEE ALSO: Boba Fett

Eye sensor allows Jango to see behind him

Fett is an expert pilot and teaches his son Boba from an early age.

Segmented armor plate allows flexibility

Gauntlet projectile dart shooter

ESPITE HAVING no affiliation with Mandalore, Jango Fett wears the rmored uniform that helped make he Mandalorians a dreaded name. During he Republic's final years, he is regarded s the best bounty hunter in the galaxy.

Fett in his ship, *Slave I*, blasts Obi-Wan Kenobi's Jedi starfighter in the Geonosis asteroid field.

Segmented armor plate

Lethal Opponent

In battle with Obi-Wan Kenobi, Fett launches himself into the air using his jetpack. He carries many weapons, including knee pad rocket launchers, and wrist gauntlets that fire darts, whipcords, and blades.

FETT'S REPUTATION as a supreme warrior led the Kaminoans to recruit him for their secret army project: every clone trooper is a clone of him. Fett receives a lucrative amount of credits, but also requests one unaltered clone to raise as his son.

JAR JAR BINKS

ROGUE GUNGAN TURNED SENATOR

DATA FILE

AFFILIATION: Gungan Grand Army, Republic
HOMEWORLD: Naboo
SPECIES: Gungan
HEIGHT: 1.96m (6ft 5in)
APPEARANCES: I, II, CW, III
SEE ALSO: Qui-Gon Jinn; Padmé Amidala

Haillu (earlobes) for display

JAR JAR BINKS is an amphibious Gungan from Naboo. During the invasion of Naboo, Jedi Qui-Gon Jinn runs into and rescues Jar Jar. Jar Jar becomes a general in the Gungan Grand Army, and then a Junior Representative in the Galactic Senate.

At first, clumsy Jar Jar proves more of a hindrance than a help at the Battle of Naboo.

During the Clone Wars, Jar Jar goes on many diplomatic missions to aid the Republic.

Cast-off stretchy Gungan pants

Powerful calf muscles for swimming

JAR JAR is well-meaning but accident-prone. This simple soul is elevated to a position in the Senate that may be beyond his abilities. Luckily for him, the Naboo value purity of heart over other qualifications to govern.

Tight trouser ends keep out swamp crawlies

Good Intentions

In Padmé's absence, Jar Jar represents Naboo in the Senate. With the best of intentions, Jar Jar sets in motion a new galactic era as he proposes a motion for Supreme Chancellor Palpatine to accept emergency powers to deal with the Separatist threat.

LANDO CALRISSIAN

BARON ADMINISTRATOR OF CLOUD CITY

DATA FILE

AFFILIATION: Rebel Alliance
HOMEWORLD: Unknown
SPECIES: Human
HEIGHT: 1.78m (5ft 10in)
APPEARANCES: R, V, VI
SEE ALSO: Han Solo

Borrowed
rebel blaster

Tarelle
sel-weave shirt

Royal emblems

Lando disguises himself as a lowly
skiff guard at Jabba's palace to
aid in the rescue of Han Solo.

DASHING LANDO CALRISSIAN
is a rogue, con artist, smuggler,
and gambler, who won control
of Cloud City in a game of
sabacc. He has come to
enjoy his newfound
sense of responsibility
as Baron Administrator.

LANDO'S Cloud City
is a fabulous mining colony
on Bespin. After leaving the
city, Lando falls in with the
rebels. He is promoted to
General and still finds
adventure, but now
contributes his abilities
to a greater cause.

After Han's capture, Lando
joins Chewbacca to
search for his old friend.

Betrayed

Calrissian is forced to betray Han Solo and
his friends to Darth Vader in order to
preserve Cloud City's freedom. When he
learns that the Sith Lord has no intention
of keeping his side of the bargain, Lando
plots a rescue mission and escapes
from the city he once ruled.

LUKE SKYWALKER

THE LAST JEDI

DATA FILE

AFFILIATION: Jedi
HOMEWORLD: Tatooine
SPECIES: Human
HEIGHT: 1.72m (5ft 8in)
APPEARANCES: III, IV, V, VI, VII
SEE ALSO: Princess Leia; Han Solo; Yoda; Darth Vader

In close combat with Darth Vader, Luke discovers the truth about his father.

Tatooine farm tunic

Anakin Skywalker's lightsaber

Droid caller

Tool pouch

TATOOINE FARMHAND Luke Skywalker is thrown into a world of adventure when he discovers a secret message inside one of his new droids. Luke becomes a space pilot for the Rebel Alliance and fulfills his true destiny as a legendary Jedi Knight.

AFTER THE Empire is defeated, Luke undertakes much study, travel, and spiritual contemplation, before committing to pass his knowledge on to a new generation of Jedi students. The reestablishment of the Jedi Order, however, suffers a terrible setback with the coming of Kylo Ren.

Jedi Path

Luke first climbs into the cockpit of an X-wing in the attack on the first Death Star. Fighting for the Rebel Alliance in the years afterward, Luke becomes great leader. Yoda helps to awake Luke's Force abilities, and, as a Jed Luke faces the challenges of the Emperor and Vader, holding the galaxy's hope for freedom.

LUMINARA UNDULI

MIRIALAN JEDI MASTER

DATA FILE

AFFILIATION: Jedi
HOMEWORLD: Mirial
SPECIES: Mirialan
HEIGHT: 1.7m (5ft 7in)
APPEARANCES: II, CW, III, R
SEE ALSO: Yoda

Traditional
Mirialan
headdress

Luminara Unduli serves on Kashyyyk until she is captured by clone troopers during Order 66.

BORN ON THE COLD, dry world of Mirial, Luminara Unduli joined the Jedi Order at a young age. She fights against Count Dooku's droid soldiers at the Battle of Geonosis and is one of the few Jedi to survive the onslaught. Unduli serves as a Jedi General in the Clone Wars.

Mirialan
facial tattoo

Form III
lightsaber position

Battle on Geonosis

Luminara Unduli and more than 200 other Jedi fight Count Dooku's army in the Geonosis arena. When Jedi Master Yoda arrives with the newly created clone army, Unduli quickly takes command of a unit of soldiers to wage war in a great land battle against the Separatists.

LUMINARA UNDULI dies in an Imperial prison on Stygeon Prime. The Grand Inquisitor uses rumors of her survival and the lingering Force presence of her remains to draw out Jedi survivors.

OBI-WAN KENOBI

LEGENDARY JEDI MASTER

DATA FILE

AFFILIATION: Jedi
HOMEWORLD: Stewjon
SPECIES: Human
HEIGHT: 1.79m (5ft 10in)
APPEARANCES: I, II, CW, III, R, IV, V, VI
SEE ALSO: Anakin Skywalker; Luke Skywalker

Under-tunic

Jedi robe

Kenobi faces Darth Vader—once Kenobi's Padawan, Anakin Skywalker—in battle.

Kenobi's lightsaber skills are legendary

OBI-WAN KENOBI is a truly great Jedi who finds himself at the heart of galactic turmoil as the Republic unravels and finally collapses. Although cautious by nature, Kenobi has a healthy independen streak and truly formidable lightsaber skills.

KENOBI'S path is destined to lead in a very different direction to that of his Jedi partner, Anakin Skywalker. After Order 66, Kenobi helps protect Luke and Leia Skywalker. For many years, he remains in hiding on Tatooine, watching over Luke Skywalker, the last hope for the ancient Jedi Order.

General Kenobi

Kenobi becomes a great Jedi General and pilot in the Clone Wars (despite being a reluctant flier!). Trained by the headstrong Qui-Gon Jinn, Kenobi train his own master's protégé, Anakin Skywalker, after Jinn's death. The bon between Obi-Wan and Anakin is stro as they fight through the Clone Wars.

Obi-Wan's considered approach to situations often conflicts with Anakin's brash nature.

PADMÉ AMIDALA

NABOO QUEEN AND SENATOR

Hair pulled tightly back for clear view of enemy

DATA FILE

AFFILIATION: Royal House of Naboo, Galactic Senate
HOMEWORLD: Naboo
SPECIES: Human
HEIGHT: 1.65m (5ft 5in)
APPEARANCES: I, II, CW, III
SEE ALSO: Anakin Skywalker

Slashes in clothing sustained in Geonosian arena battle

PADMÉ GREW

up in a small Naboo village. Exceptionally talented, she was elected queen at the age of only 14. At the end of her term of office, Padmé is made Senator of Naboo. It is on the Galactic capital, Coruscant, that she becomes closer to Anakin Skywalker.

PADMÉ AMIDALA HAS TIME and again found herself at the center of galactic events. From the invasion of her home planet, Naboo, to a death sentence in a Geonosian arena, by way of multiple attempts on her life as a Senator, Padmé faces extraordinary danger with determination and great bravery.

Padmé and Anakin surrender to the love they share, though they know it breaks Jedi rules.

Light shin armor

Action boots with firm grip

Queen Turned Fighter

As the young Queen of Naboo, Padmé Amidala has to learn that her cherished values of non-violence will not save her people from a brutal droid invasion. Discarding her formal robes of state, Padmé determines to inspire her own troops to end the invasion by capturing the Neimoidian leaders.

PALPATINE

SITH LORD AND GALACTIC EMPEROR

DATA FILE

AFFILIATION: Sith, Republic/Empire
HOMEWORLD: Naboo
SPECIES: Human
HEIGHT: 1.78m (5ft 10in)
APPEARANCES: I, II, CW, III, R, V, VI
SEE ALSO: Darth Vader

Hood to hide face

Palpatine secretly plans the Clone Wars to destroy the Galactic Republic and the Jedi Order.

PALPATINE is known by many names. Born on Naboo, Sheev Palpatine becomes his homeworld's Senator. Then, he is Supreme Chancellor Palpatine. Finally, he declares himself Emperor and rules the galaxy. Ultimate power has been his plan all along. Palpatine is secretly Darth Sidious, the most evil of Sith Lords.

PALPATINE

manages to keep all those around him from suspecting his true identity. For years, he has appeared patient and unassuming, so few have recognized his political ambitions. His dark side powers even blinded the Jedi from seeing behind his mask of affability.

Sensing Vader's defeat on Mustafar, Palpatine travels to his apprentice's side.

Sith Powers

His face twisted and scarred by the dark energies of the Force, Emperor Palpatine is a figure of terrible power. One of his most deadly weapons Sith lightning, which is projected from his fingertip A Force user can block the lethal energy for a whi if they are strong, but it takes immense effort.

PRINCESS LEIA

GENERAL OF THE RESISTANCE

DATA FILE

AFFILIATION: Rebel Alliance/Resistance
HOMEWORLD: Alderaan
SPECIES: Human
HEIGHT: 1.55m (5ft 1in)
APPEARANCES: III, IV, V, VI, VII
SEE ALSO: Luke Skywalker; Han Solo

AS SENATOR for Alderaan, Princess Leia Organa made diplomatic missions across the galaxy on her ship, the *Tantive IV*. Secretly, Leia worked for the Rebel Alliance, and she played a vital role in the defeat of the Empire.

Resistance uniform

RAISED ON Alderaan by her adoptive father, Bail Organa, Leia was well prepared for her royal position, and used her high-placed connections wherever she could to aid the Alliance. During the decades of peace that follow the destruction of the Empire, Leia is able to concentrate on her new family, but as the galaxy once again undergoes turmoil, she returns to her role as a military commander.

Decisive Leader

Leia was a key command figure in the Rebel Alliance, overseeing important missions and planning strategy, alongside General Rieekan and other Alliance leaders. In Echo Base on Hoth, Leia peered intently at the scanners, alert to any signs of Imperial detection.

Leia commands the Resistance from its hidden base on the planet D'Qar.

Travel boots

QUI-GON JINN

JEDI WHO DISCOVERS "THE CHOSEN ONE"

DATA FILE

AFFILIATION: Jedi
HOMEWORLD: Coruscant
SPECIES: Human
HEIGHT: 1.93m (6ft 4in)
APPEARANCES: I, II, CW
SEE ALSO: Anakin Skywalker

Qui-Gon Jinn is one of the few Jedi to have battled a Sith—Darth Maul.

Long hair worn back to keep vision clear

QUI-GON JINN

is an experienced but headstrong Jedi Master. He was Padawan to Count Dooku and teacher to Obi-Wan Kenobi. Jinn has sometimes clashed with the Jedi High Council over his favoring of risk and action: as a result, he has not been offered a seat on the Council.

Jedi tunic

Jinn's dying wish is that Obi-Wan trains Anakin.

The Chosen One

When Jinn encounters young Anakin Skywalker, he believes he has discovered the prophesied individual who will bring balance to the Force. Jinn makes a bet with slave owner Watto: if the boy wins his podrace, then he also wins his freedom. If he loses, Jinn loses his ship. The risk pays off, and Jinn takes the boy to Coruscant to present him to the Jedi High Council, with mixed results.

QUI-GON JINN

fights actively for the Galactic Republic, but he is struck down by the unruly dark energies of Darth Maul. After his death, Jinn becomes the first Jedi to live on in the Force, a gift he will pass on to Obi-Wan Kenobi, Yoda, and Anakin Skywalker.

Rugged travel boots

R2-D2

THE BRAVEST DROID IN THE GALAXY

DATA FILE

AFFILIATION: Republic/
Rebel Alliance/Resistance
TYPE: R-2 series
astromech droid
MANUFACTURER: Industrial
Automaton
HEIGHT: 1.09m (3ft 7in)
APPEARANCES: I, II, CW,
III, R, IV, V, VI, VII
SEE ALSO: C-3PO;
Princess Leia

R2-D2 IS NO ORDINARY astromech droid. His long history of adventures has given him a distinct personality. He is stubborn and inventive, and is strongly motivated to succeed at any given task. Although R2-D2 speaks only in electronic beeps and whistles, he usually manages to make his point!

Holographic projector

R2-D2 has many hidden tricks, including extension arms and rocket boosters.

R2-D2 first distinguishes himself on board Queen Amidala's Royal Starship. He serves Anakin Skywalker during the Clone Wars and then Luke Skywalker during the Rebellion, flying in the droid socket of their spaceships.

Powerbus cables

Motorized, all-terrain treads

Risky Mission

At the end of the Clone Wars, R2-D2 is assigned to Bail Organa's diplomatic fleet. Princess Leia entrusts R2-D2 with the stolen Death Star plans and her urgent message to Obi-Wan Kenobi. He risks all kinds of damage to accomplish his mission.

TARFFUL

WOOKIEE CHIEFTAIN

Teeth bared
for war cry

DATA FILE

AFFILIATION: Republic
HOMEWORLD: Kashyyyk
SPECIES: Wookiee
HEIGHT: 2.34m (7ft 8in)
APPEARANCES: CW, III
SEE ALSO: Chewbacca

TARFFUL IS LEADER of the Wookiee city of Kachirho. When the Separatist forces invade his planet, Kashyyyk, Tarfful work: with Chewbacca and Jedi Yoda, Luminara Unduli, and Quinlan Vos to plan the Wookiees' strategy for repelling the invaders.

Decorative
pauldron

Orb-igniter

Tarfful and Chewbacca help Yoda flee in a hidden escape pod after Order 66.

TARFFUL WAS

once enslaved by the Trandoshan slavers, who have long been the enemies of the Wookiees. When clone troops rescued him, Tarfful pledged to fight anyone who tried to enslave his people or capture his planet.

Thick calf
muscles from
climbing trees

Fur protects
upper foot

Wookiee Attack

Tarfful is a calm, considerate Wookiee who can be a mighty warrior when necessary. He leads his fellow Wookiees in daring raids on amphibious Separatist tank droids.

YODA

LEGENDARY JEDI MASTER

YODA IS ONE OF THE most powerful Jedi ever, and has lived to be nearly 900 years old. He served the Galactic Republic at its height, as well as through its decline and fall. Yoda is one of the few Jedi to survive the Clone Wars—he goes into hiding on the remote planet Dagobah.

DATA FILE

Head has been nearly bald for centuries

AFFILIATION: Jedi
HOMEWORLD: Unknown
SPECIES: Unknown
HEIGHT: 66cm (2ft 2in)
APPEARANCES: I, II, CW, III, R, V, VI
SEE ALSO: Luke Skywalker

Homespun robe

YODA HAS

guided hundreds of Jedi to knighthood and visited countless worlds. He takes quiet satisfaction in his ability to resolve conflict by nonviolent means, until the re-emergence of the dark side unseats others' confidence in him.

Sith Fury

Accepting finally that the Clone Wars have been nothing more than a manipulation by the Sith to destroy the Jedi Order, Yoda confronts Palpatine. Even the diminutive Jedi's amazing strength and speed, however, are not a match for the devastating fury of a Sith Lord.

On Dagobah, Yoda trains Luke Skywalker, his final student and the galaxy's last hope.

Anakin, Yoda, and Obi-Wan become one with the Force after their deaths.

INDEX

ACKNOWLEDGMENTS

Penguin Random House

Editors Pamela Afram, Ruth Amos, Jo Casey,
Hannah Dolan, David Fentiman, Rahul Ganguly,
Emma Grange, Matt Jones, Julia March,
Lisa Stock, Victoria Taylor, Arushi Vats
Designers Owen Bennett, Dan Bunyan, Jon Hall,
Richard Horsford, Akansha Jain, David McDonald,
Lynne Moulding, Sandra Perry, Umesh Singh Rawat,
Clive Savage, Suzena Sengupta, Rajdeep Singh,
Lisa Sodeau, Rhys Thomas, Toby Truphet
Senior Pre-Production Producer Siu Yin Chan
Senior Producer Gary Batchelor
Managing Editors Laura Gilbert, Sadie Smith,
Chitra Subramanyam
Managing Art Editors Neha Ahuja,
Maxine Pedliham, Ron Stobbart
Creative Manager Sarah Harland
Art Director Lisa Lanzarini
Publisher Julie Ferris
Publishing Director Simon Beecroft

Reading Consultant Linda Gambrell, PhD.

For Lucasfilm
Executive Editor Jonathan W. Rinzler
Story Group Pablo Hidalgo, Leland Chee, Rayne Roberts
Image Archives Tina Mills, Stacey Leong, Matthew Azeveda,
Shahana Alam
Art Director Troy Alders
Director of Publishing Carol Roeder

Dorling Kindersley would like to thank Elizabeth Dowsett and Joel Kempson
for editorial assistance, and Anne Sharples for design assistance.

First American Edition, 2016
Published in the United States by DK Publishing
345 Hudson Street, New York, New York 10014
DK, a Division of Penguin Random House LLC

Contains content previously published in *Star Wars: Character Encyclopedia: Updated
and Expanded* (2016) and *Star Wars: Jedi Battles* (2014)

001-299277-June/2016

Page design copyright © 2016 Dorling Kindersley Limited

© & TM 2016 LUCASFILM LTD.

A catalog record for this book is available from the Library of Congress.

ISBN 978-1-4654-5882-7

Printed and bound in China

www.dk.com
www.starwars.com

A WORLD OF IDEAS:
SEE ALL THERE IS TO KNOW